SUE PIETERS-HAWKE was born in Canberra in 1957 and grew up in Melbourne. She has studied law, history, complementary health and healing, yoga, qigong and Tibetan Buddhism. While raising her two children, she worked part time as a publicist/fundraiser and project manager, and she established a clinic and school with two Chinese qigong masters. She has run Hazel Hawke's office since 1995. Sue lives in Sydney with her daughter and their cat, and works as a freelance project consultant, writer and public speaker.

HAZEL FLYNN is a writer, editor, publisher, radio broadcaster and book reviewer. She lives in Sydney.

# HAZEL'S JOURNEY

*A personal experience of Alzheimer's*

SUE PIETERS-HAWKE

AND HAZEL FLYNN

MACMILLAN
Pan Macmillan Australia

First published 2004 in Macmillan by Pan Macmillan Australia Pty Limited
St Martins Tower, 31 Market Street, Sydney

Reprinted 2004 (five times)



National Library of Australia
Cataloguing-in-Publication data:

Pieters-Hawke, Sue.
Hazel's journey : a personal experience of Alzheimer's.

ISBN 1 40503631 1.

1. Hawke, Hazel. 2. Alzheimer's disease - Patients - Australia - Biography. 3. Prime ministers' spouses - Australia - Biography. I. Title.

362.1968310092

Papers used by Pan Macmillan Australia Pty Ltd are natural, recyclable products made from wood grown in sustainable forests. The manufacturing processes conform to the environmental regulations of the country of origin.

Set in 12 pt Janson by Midland Typesetters, Maryborough, Victoria
Printed in Australia by McPherson's Printing Group, Maryborough, Victoria

*For Mum,*
*and for everyone living with Alzheimer's.*
– SPH

*For Ricky and our darlings, Cormac and Augusta,*
*and for my mother, Marie.*
– HF

# Contents

# Foreword

'It's a bugger . . . It's just bad luck. You could get rheumatic fever, or lose a leg or something – all sorts of things happen . . . People get all sorts of disadvantage which comes from an illness: some of them are never the same again. They can't do stuff they used to. But they don't become social outcasts or write-offs . . .

I've got no embarrassment about it being a shameful thing, because it's got nothing to do with shame. It's an illness, which is unpredictable and when it comes you've just got to cope with it. And the more research that's done – and money that's raised in order to do research – the more it might be, well, not eradicated, but dealt with in better ways to assist people with Alzheimer's. Because it's very difficult. It's like losing your skin or something. But in fact you lose some of your head – your works [laughs].'

Hazel Hawke in conversation about having
Alzheimer's disease, on 20 July 2004, her 75th birthday.

# How You Can Help

It is estimated that by 2050 there will be half a million Australians diagnosed with dementia. (Alzheimer's is the most common form of dementia, accounting for 70 per cent of cases.)

**We need to do more** to improve the lives of those with the disease, to improve our understanding and management of it, and to search for a cure.

**You can help by donating to the Hazel Hawke Alzheimer's Research and Care Fund.**

The fund is administered by Alzheimer's Australia, and overseen by an independent advisory board that includes Hazel's representatives.

**To donate** phone 1300 306 293. Send a cheque or money order payable to the Hazel Hawke Alzheimer's Research and Care Fund to PO Box 108, Higgins, ACT, 2615. Or log on to the fund website, www.hazelhawke.net.au and either make a secure online donation or download and print a credit card donation form.

**If you have bought this book, thank you** – part of the purchase price has been donated to the work of the fund. We are extremely grateful for whatever extra donation you can make.

# Preface

This is not a story I wanted to tell. I wish it was the second volume of my mother's autobiography you were about to read – her own version of the life she looked forward to after leaving Canberra and my father. But that book cannot be written.

Mum has never felt inclined to air the intimate details of her life simply because she became a public figure. When public revelations of things she'd rather keep private have been thrust upon her, she has coped with as much grace as possible. And when she believed that talking about something very personal might help others in a similar situation, she has overcome her natural reticence and done so.

In November 2003 she overcame her doubts and fears to go public about something very personal and distressing: she let it be known that she was suffering from Alzheimer's disease. She chose to do this, via the ABC-TV program *Australian Story*, because she thought that speaking out might make a positive contribution. She hoped that by showing that living with Alzheimer's doesn't mean the end of life, love or dignity, it might help people to understand and support those affected by it. And that others, as yet untouched, might want to help by donating money for care and research.

The response to the show, 'The Big A', was overwhelming. Millions of people watched it and were moved and inspired. A flood of kind thoughts and shared stories poured in. People generously donated to the fund we set up in Mum's name to help fight the disease. And we heard directly and indirectly from many, many people, sufferers and carers alike, that it really had made a difference.

Dementia in general, and Alzheimer's in particular, has long been fraught with fear, embarrassment, shame and grief. Not surprisingly, personal stories about its effects have been few and far between. Unless you happen to have dealt with it directly you are unlikely to have any real idea what it is like to face the slow degeneration of the brain, the progressive loss of the very things that seem to make you, you. It was clear from the response to Mum's 'coming out' that there is a hunger to know more. To know what it's really like to live with the disease, and to find out how Mum is coping with its challenges.

Mum has always been fired by the need to 'do her bit'. From a modest, happy childhood in Perth she went on to become one of the most loved occupants of The Lodge in Canberra, in part because people could see her sincere desire to make a constructive contribution. But no matter how well known or popular she became, she never lost her sense of being one among many – a person who encountered some extraordinary circumstances, but didn't view herself differently because of that. She simply made the most of the opportunities that came her way and did her best to cope with the difficulties.

Her life now is, once again, a very private one. She is no longer inclined to speak about it in the public arena. But she is fierce in her desire that 'the bloody A thing', as she sometimes calls it, be destigmatised; that we do what we can as a community to help people living with it, and that we support research aimed at improving management of the disease and maybe, ultimately, prevention or cure. And that is why this book exists. There is a promising body of research under way that does offer hope – but with no cure likely in the near future, we urgently need to find a better way to deal with the impact of Alzheimer's in our society. What you are holding in your hands now is our attempt to contribute to that.

The responsibility of telling Mum's story (and, after some persuasion, parts of my own that pertain to it) feels weighty, one I have approached with some trepidation. I do not want to suggest that this is 'the whole story'. It can't be; it's just one perspective, and other family and friends will naturally have their own. It has certainly been a confronting process, given its emotional nature, but also because I have become habituated, over the years, to guarding family privacy when it comes to personal issues. But this is as full a picture as I can provide of how I have seen things unfold.

The effect of the Alzheimer's is such that knowledge of this book is not something Mum has with her all the time. But whenever it does come up her response is strong, almost a mantra: 'Yes, we must do whatever we can to decrease stigma and increase funding.' I am reminded of the first day Hazel

Flynn came to my home so that we could start work. Mum lives next door and she wandered in at lunchtime, as she does, for a chat. I introduced the two Hazels and reminded Mum about the book. For a moment she couldn't think what we were talking about, then it jogged back into place. 'Are you sure you don't mind me doing the book, Mum?' I asked. 'Oh no!' she said. 'If you've got it you might as well talk about it. You can do it for me.' Then, turning to a young man who was visiting my daughter, she belly-laughed and made sure she had his attention before adding, 'But cross your fingers you don't get it. It's a bugger!'

Sue Pieters-Hawke

CHAPTER 1

# 'Bugger, Bugger, Bugger!'

WE WERE PARKING AT Royal North Shore Private Hospital in Sydney on our way to see Dr Terry Finnegan. In one sense it was simply another doctor's appointment. I'd sat in a lot of consulting rooms and clinics with Mum by then, for health matters ranging from simple osteopathic visits to ongoing complications arising from major surgery. So there was, on the surface, a matter-of-factness, a familiar routine. But at the same time, we both knew that it promised – or threatened – to be something much more.

It was 21 September 2001, a sunny spring day. Driving along, Mum had been a little subdued, lost in her own thoughts, but as I turned off the engine, she 'came to' and her attention settled on a plant in front of the car. 'Oh, that bush is looking good!' she said, with warm familiarity. Mum is very attuned to plants and gardens wherever she goes. She has always been a keen gardener and she regards the plants in her own garden as entertaining characters. The trouble was we'd never seen that bush before.

She was having what I had come to think of as a false déjà vu: a feeling of recognition when the person or thing concerned was, in fact, new to her. When I saw what was happening it hit me yet again how profoundly Mum's perceptions and her ability to interpret the world around her were changing.

As we went up to the consulting suites, Mum was again quiet, while I was feeling a heightened sensitivity, an impotent desire to protect her privacy in such a public space at such a private time. Her face tends to be recognised wherever we go, and people are lovely to her – she seems to inspire friendly admiration and an easy familiarity. But public recognition in the supermarket is one thing, the risk of it happening while visiting a geriatrician, as we were now about to do, is a very different prospect.

Still, the other people in the shared waiting area were there with their own problems, and no-one seemed to pay us any attention. As we waited I noticed Mum had put on odd shoes – both black and of a similar style, but clearly from different pairs. Oops. Not that it really mattered – but it was another small sign, insignificant in itself but representative of the sense of 'slippage' that had slowly led us to this point.

Soon we were being greeted by Dr Finnegan and shown in to his room. My usual practice at times like this was to sit to the side and slightly behind Mum, out of respect for her. Yes, she might have come to need my assistance in these situations, and I'll admit that I was starting to have to shake my head discreetly out of her field of vision when she gave an inaccurate answer to a question about her medical history or daily life, for instance, but this was her consultation, not mine.

We were both very aware of why we were there. Mum had been complaining about her memory not being up to scratch. Those of us close to her had noticed significant changes in the way she was thinking and dealing with day-to-day life. We had previously been reassured by medical experts that the changes were a side effect of her surgeries and personal stress, and were nothing to worry further about. But it was clear by now that there was cause for concern, that something else was going on.

So she had been referred by her GP, Dr Richard Schloeffel, to Dr Finnegan, who would further interpret the results of tests previously performed by neuropsychologist Robyn Murray. The tests were designed to identify what kinds of changes were happening in Mum's brain, and to suggest probable causes. Nine years earlier, a benign tumour had been found in her pituitary gland and had been removed. The possibility of another brain tumour was a valid one, as were several other conditions, including Alzheimer's disease, which Robyn thought was the most likely explanation.

Dr Finnegan took Mum's medical history and talked to her about her concerns, then administered an additional short, simple, but telling test. It was clearly designed to test memory and mental acuity and featured straightforward questions such as: 'What's the date? Where are you? How did you get here?' It also required her to remember number sequences forwards and backwards, and then remember them five minutes later, and so on. Watching her do it, I could see that she was working hard on trying to 'pass'.

I'd known for quite a while that she was doing her best to keep everything going as it had been. Some of her faculties weren't operating nearly as well as they used to and she knew it so, typically, her response was to work harder at it. There was also a defensive, deflecting technique that she had developed for dealing with questions she felt she should know the answer to, but didn't, which was an air of 'Oh, that's ridiculous. What's wrong with you that you're asking me this?'

But, of course, nothing could change the truth, and the truth, as we were about to hear, was that yes, Mum did have a major problem.

When the short test was finished, Mum excused herself to go to the loo. Dr Finnegan took the opportunity to speak quietly to me before she returned. 'I think your mother does have Alzheimer's disease,' he said. He added that it wasn't possible to be certain (as I now know, the only definitive way to know is to examine the brain after death). But he was as sure as the weight of his experience could allow him to be. In telling me this he was kind, gentle but direct, and clearly knowledgeable. But there was an awful mismatch, a weird sense of dissonance between the news that was being delivered – something so intimate and so powerfully affecting – and the fact that we were getting that news from a doctor we'd never met before, in an appointment lasting half an hour or so, and then off we would go back to our lives to deal with it. I'm sure many people have experienced something similar: recognising or wondering if there's a problem, going through a series of tests and then going to a specialist's office for 'the verdict', and in a few minutes of conversation with a stranger your life changes irrevocably. It is surreal.

But there was nothing surreal about the news itself. The impact of the word Alzheimer's was like a body blow. It was horrible. I felt it physically, as a shadow passing through my stomach and then over my whole body. It wasn't that I'd been nursing a reasonable hope of finding out nothing was wrong, because there was clearly something going on and it had a steady, progressive quality. My discussions with Robyn Murray had prepared me for the strong probability it was Alzheimer's. And, even before Robyn's report, some of us had started to face the fact that Mum did have some sort of degenerative or progressive condition that affected memory and cognitive capacity. We had begun to come to terms with that. But coming to terms has so many layers and levels and, even if you think you're ready for it, the effect of a formal diagnosis, a label, can be almost overpowering.

Alzheimer's is a particularly crushing diagnosis to be given. It carries heavy baggage – the spectre of inevitability, of helpless degeneration and loss of self. Such scary imagery. There is a sense of fear and dread associated with it, compounded by the vague idea that there's 'not a lot that can be done to counter the disease'. It's one of those diagnoses that seems to offer little sense of hope or escape. That's what makes it so hard to hear.

Mum was going to be back any minute, and this was no time to fall apart. I asked, 'What's next?' and Dr Finnegan said he would tell Mum. I remember thinking that I didn't want her to go through that – I would have done anything for it not to have to happen. But, of course, it did.

When Mum returned to the room and sat down, she asked Dr Finnegan what he thought her problem was. He talked us through the test results and then said, 'Hazel, I think you have Alzheimer's.' She didn't have a big visible reaction; she just took a moment, and then went on to ask some practical questions about the next steps and likely prognosis. But I could see that the news had made a major impact on her. There was a very still, quiet and grey quality to her. Mum was born in 1929 and she's a woman typical of her generation: reserved in some ways, with a sort of a stoic streak, particularly when it comes to dealing with any kind of personal difficulty of her own. So her reaction was a very subtle, internal one. But I had no doubt it had hit her hard, and it was awful to watch. There was a heaviness and a bleakness in the room, and most of all for me the thought, 'What is this like for Mum? What's it like for her to be sitting here, hearing this?' I felt completely powerless to make any difference, to help her at all. It was nightmarish.

We took in some of the information that Dr Finnegan was giving us in answer to our questions, but some of it was simply too much to absorb right then. One thing I do distinctly remember is him saying, when Mum asked what to expect, was that a useful guideline to the progression of the disease can be to look at how things have gone in the last six to twelve months, and from that you can get a sense of how things will go in the future. In other words, the rate of decline (that awful word) will tend to be reasonably consistent over time, albeit with ups and downs. Given what I had seen of the changes in Mum over the previous year, this was not good news.

Feeling grim, we wrapped things up with the doctor and went out to his receptionist to pay. I was conscious of being back in the public area, and I knew Mum would be too, so we didn't say anything until stepping out into the hallway. She stopped, turned and looked at me, stomped one foot and said, 'Bugger, bugger, bugger!' I put my arm around her. What was there to say? We stood silently for a long moment then, muttering something like 'We'll just take this a step at a time', we headed back down to the car, and home.

Looking back on it, that day was about following Mum's lead in accepting whatever life was throwing up at us. There is a strength of heart and character in my mother that nothing, not even Alzheimer's, can destroy, and it was never clearer than on that day. She didn't break down, or feel sorry for herself, she just got on with things, which meant that's what the rest of us did, too.

~

OF COURSE, MUM DID have a coping mechanism not readily available to the rest of us at the time: she could forget what had happened.

I drove her the short distance home from the hospital (I was then living a few minutes away from her, with my husband, Jan, and our children Sophie, who was aged 16, and Ben, 12). It was after-school time by now and I needed to go and see to the kids but I was concerned about leaving Mum alone. I stayed with her, chatting for a while, and then thought, 'Well, what am I meant to do, babysit her . . . ?' Because, of course, other than the diagnosis being handed down, nothing had changed. She was no more or less capable than she had been that morning. It was important to make sure the effect of having *received* the diagnosis wasn't hitting her so hard she needed company, but in terms of the disease itself, she was unchanged.

Looking back, I can see that this day was, for each of us in different ways, the introduction to 'the power of the label'. The potential power to shatter hope, to create fear and, perhaps worst of all, to irrevocably alter how a person perceives themselves and is perceived by others. It was the beginning of a journey characterised most of all by Mum's determined refusal to be defined, at core, by the disease, while struggling with the very real changes Alzheimer's does bring.

She was, in fact, fine about being on her own. She loves her house and she loves her freedom, and she was happy for a little solitude then. 'I'll be okay, love,' she said, and once I felt sure, I went home to see to the kids, arranging to pop back in a couple of hours.

Around dinnertime I went around to see her, and it quickly became clear she didn't fully remember what had happened. When I realised this I started probing very tentatively by asking 'How do you feel after today?', and so on. She seemed affected by what had happened – she was more subdued than usual – but I saw that she did not specifically remember much of what had occurred. She did not talk either directly about the appointment or allude to it, and when I did she just looked a bit vague, so I didn't push it. Her memory at that point in the illness was not *that* bad, so it struck me more as defensive forgetting, as a way of not having it too much 'in her face'. And I thought that was fair enough.

That continued for weeks, maybe even months – she would simply not remember what had happened. Occasionally I would do a 'test probe' to see how she was about it, but if she didn't remember or respond, I would quickly let it go. Ironically, now, when her memory and cognitive function is much worse than it was then, she is quite clear about having Alzheimer's, and at times talks freely and plainly about it. Over time it firmed up for her, and she would bring it up and we'd talk about it, but I'm sure that initial auto-erase reaction was mostly her way of coping at the time.

Mum's reaction to the official diagnosis, as muted and numbed as it might have seemed, taps in to my own mixed feelings on not having sought diagnosis sooner, and Mum's occasional irritation that we sought it at all. This is an issue that seems to give rise to rather strong and often divergent views. I am not advocating any of them – it is different for everyone concerned, and I don't think any generality can override the very personal nature of this journey. On the one hand I worry that early diagnosis carries the risk that the person with the disease and their carers will be hit with a sense of horror and stigma and inevitability of outcome that can be paralysing. That the person will be boxed, or will box themselves, into an unnecessarily limited view of what is possible in their lives. A 'premature shutdown', if you like, caused not so much by the actual effects of the disease, which tend to be very gradual over time, but by the response to being given a label.

This is something about which different people feel very differently, and that was the case among those connected with Mum – some would have preferred an earlier diagnosis, while she herself turned down earlier suggestions that seeking specialist advice might be a good idea. On the other hand, I understand that early diagnosis can be really useful in some circumstances, and that is increasingly so as therapies and medications become more effective, and hopefully as stigma lifts and attitudes change. But unless it's handled carefully, the effect of too early a diagnosis can be to make the real, everyday challenges with which you're already coping seem even more burdensome.

Mum's life was peopled with family and friends who loved her and were committed to supporting her. It had become clear before the diagnosis that she had diminishing capacities in various areas, and we had all, in our own ways, adjusted for that. So despite the major emotional toll the diagnosis took, the label didn't make any difference in that regard. But, of course, people still had to be told.

I spoke to Jan first. His family is in Europe and so Mum is like his mum in a way. She and he think the sun shines out of each other. She had already asked him to be responsible for administering her financial affairs, and given him an enduring Power of Attorney. (They'd liked each other since they first met over 20 years ago in Japan, where Jan was living at the time. Mum had arranged to meet him while there on a state visit, having heard from me about this Belgian who had taken my fancy when I was studying at a Japanese Dojo, and whom I was interested in spending more time with.) The news hit Jan as hard as it had hit me. We were shocked, but not surprised, simply because things had been leading up to this reality for a while. Amid his distress, almost immediately his thoughts turned to the practicalities of securing Mum's future.

In those first days I also discussed the diagnosis and its implications with my sister, Ros, and my brother, Steve.

Neither lived in Sydney – Ros was in Canberra, Steve near Perth with his family – but both saw Mum regularly. They took the news in their own ways, but both were, of course, upset and concerned. Prue Watson, Mum's personal assistant and a family friend, and Dr Richard Schloeffel were also concerned and supportive.

What was clear to us all was that we wanted to do whatever it took to make sure Mum continued to have a satisfying and happy time, in the house she loved so much, with as much independence as possible. That is what she wanted. We would make sure she could live, as far as possible, the life she had so happily carved out for herself after her marriage to my father, Bob, broke up and she discovered true independence for the first time.

CHAPTER 2

# Her Own Life, Really

IN 1992 MOTHER PUBLISHED her autobiography. It was called *My Own Life* and in it she wrote: 'This is my story, not my husband's. But Bob has been the major single influence on the course and tenor of my life since I was eighteen. My adult experience has been indivisible from his, as it has also been from my family, my children and friends . . .' She also wrote of the time in the late 1970s when their relationship seemed to have reached breaking point: 'I did not want to leave the marriage, even though it was in a fragile state. One thing, however, was clear to me. I did not intend to be one of those middle-aged women whose husbands discard them when they have served their purpose.'

This time of turmoil passed and, in moving to Canberra, my parents renewed some of the bonds and shared goals that had grown out of their initial attraction as teenagers in 1948.

At the time of writing her story she and Dad had known each other for more than 40 years. With my father out of the Lodge, and the home they had built in Sydney almost ready, Mum wrote about the life she looked forward to: 'Our house will hang on the slope of the hill, a dangle of rooms embracing the northern sun and the view of sparkling blue water . . . We two sexagenarians have gathered just a touch of moss, but not nearly enough to stop us rolling busily, contentedly, on – with each other, our children and theirs – in our little bit of magic.'

But we now know all too well, that's not the way it went. My father was prime minister for nearly nine years, and my mother's face is just as well recognised as Dad's, but in all other respects they are, of course, just like everyone else. They'd had hopes and dreams for a life together, and their relationship, despite its fair share of ups and downs, lasted longer than many. Because of who they are, too much of the private pain associated with their split took place in the public eye. But in many ways theirs was just a perfectly ordinary, very sad and hurtful break up.

Life as the PM's wife was a busy and demanding time for Mum, but it was also very fulfilling. Her belief in the fundamental human need to 'be involved' has been a key part of her life. She has always been driven to make a contribution, reaching out to people and helping in whatever way she can. Being in Canberra gave her the scope to take this to a new level. Her profile there meant she could provide and build support for an enormous range of causes, including the environment, family life, women and children, indigenous affairs, music and cultural expression, and many corners of disadvantage in our society. Her energy and enthusiasm for that work never wavered. At the same time, she maintained strong ties with family and friends, and built new and rewarding friendships.

But 1991, their last year in the Lodge, was certainly stressful for Mum. She stood by Dad while he faced one unsuccessful leadership challenge followed by months of uncertainty. Meanwhile they were also arranging to buy the home in Sydney where they planned to base their life after politics. This task fell to Mum and had to be done as discreetly as possible because Dad was still in office and too many people would have mistakenly 'beaten up' the purchase as a signal he wanted to step down. She began feeling unusually tired and run-down and this proved to be due to a major ovarian cyst, which she had removed in November of that year. Then, in December, came a second leadership challenge to Dad; this one was successful.

After a year of uncertainty about the future, Mum and Dad had to face packing up and leaving the life and home they had known in Canberra. Plans for renovating their house in Sydney turned to plans for demolishing and creating a new house from scratch, the building of which took longer than scheduled, so what was to have been a two-month stay at a hotel while the house was being finished and fitted out went on for nearly two years. And while a luxury hotel is a great place to spend a weekend, or even a week, it's far from the home Mum had envisaged. Mum had shown great capacity to 'bounce back' in the past, but her health was not returning as well as we had all hoped, and in early 1992 she was diagnosed with a tumour in her pituitary gland. She underwent a major operation to remove it. The operation was a success – the tumour was benign – but three months later she had to go back into hospital for more brain surgery to treat a spinal fluid leak that developed, and the recovery from this operation was much more difficult than had been predicted.

But finally, in the second half of 1993, Mum and Dad moved into their 'little bit of magic'. Unfortunately, by then their marriage was again showing serious strain. Things were not turning out the way Mum had hoped when she wrote of her vision for the future. She was clearly not 100 per cent well – the multiple surgeries and major dislocations had had an impact on her resilience. And Dad was undergoing his own major adjustments. There was a palpable discord between the two of them and it was getting worse, not better, even though they were in the new house. There was a lot of pressure on Mum; getting the house built was a major project and, given the size of it, so was fitting it out. And there was a level of tension and, I think, unresolved ambiguity between Mum and Dad about what exactly they were creating. Despite the positive approach she brought to it in her autobiography, I don't think it was Mum's idea of a family home. It is certainly a beautiful house. But it wasn't really her scale of things. She loved the location, the bush and the birds and the water, and she loved the proximity to family, but her ideal home would probably have been something cosier.

At first the tensions and difficulties felt familiar, and so it seemed to be just another turbulent period, and one they would most likely get through, as they had so often before. But gradually it became clear that this time things were different.

One of the most striking aspects of my parents' relationship was their shared sense of purpose. Whatever the dissonance in their personalities and lifestyle inclinations, they had always been strongly aligned in many of their values and ways they viewed the world. It reflected, perhaps, the way they'd both been brought up in the Congregational church. And in Dad's case, the Labor Party – another 'church' whose ethos Mum wholeheartedly embraced. These shared values of friendship, community, decency and social justice, and the sense that life's purpose arises from personal contribution to these goals, had always been remarkably strong in them as individuals. But together they were formidable – committed to bringing about changes they thought would make the world a better place, focused in their approach and determined in overcoming obstacles. That shared sensibility underpinned the survival of their relationship at times when other aspects of the marriage were strained or unsatisfying. Now that they were no longer immersed either in raising a family, or in politics, it started to become clear that they had different visions of what the rest of their lives would hold.

While their general plan was to be together while continuing to pursue their own interests as they always had, the divergence between those interests was becoming greater and the common ground wearing terminally thin. Mum wanted to make a home, create a wonderful garden, spend as much time as possible with her children and grandchildren, continue to work for the causes she believed in, and have time for friends, music and maybe some golf. Dad, however, wanted to plunge into business, to travel and to explore the many corporate and community offers that were coming his way now that he was a free agent.

At first they each, in their own way, resisted the momentum that was building, but by mid-1994, they agreed to separate. For a time they lived separately in the house, but then, by agreement, Dad moved out, giving Mum a few months to sort out her affairs before she would move out and he would move back in. He also effectively bought out Mum's share of the house and she set about finding a place of her own.

She and I put together a checklist of the things she wanted in her new place – a garden or a balcony big enough to grow plants and to feel part of the outdoors, enough room for grandkids to sleep over and a place secure enough so she didn't have to be worried about living alone. She was initially focused on townhouses and units. I started looking but by the time she had to move out of the house she had shared with Dad, we still hadn't found anything suitable, so she moved in with me and Jan and the kids.

The whole period leading up to the separation and following it was a very, very difficult one for Mum. There was a lot of bitterness and anger, as there is in many marriage splits. There was, too, deep grief that came with the collapse of her hopes and dreams; she was mourning the loss of the life she had seen herself living. It was a time of fragility and sadness. I ached for her.

It proved to be a testing time in our relationship too, simply because of the difficulties of living together. We're not alone in this, I know – it's a rare adult child who can live again with a parent without one or the other eyeing the door! We laugh about it now, but those four months were one of the very few occasions I've had a rocky time getting on with Mum. I understood how she felt: she'd just come out of having and running her own life, her own domain, and she was shaken from the break-up. But both she and I are very attached to our own space, grounded in our sense of 'home'. Not in a hostile or aggressive way, but my house is my little fiefdom, and it's the same for her. She was suffering the loss of a 'place of her own' and, although she was too polite to put it directly, it was clear she wasn't enjoying having to share territory. She felt like a fish in the wrong tank. Everybody tried hard, but things definitely improved when Mum found a suitable place to buy – her very own home, for the first time in her life.

It was a place I'd looked at months before, thinking it might work for her. But it was a house, not a unit or townhouse, so it didn't fit the brief. It had, in the interim, gone to auction and been passed in. A real estate agent who was now handling it, and who didn't know I'd seen it before, suggested I take Mum to see it. (As ever when I was helping Mum with something like this and wanted privacy, I used the surname Pieters and left her name out of it.) Just as I had when I'd seen it previously, Mum liked the house straight away. It was large enough to have plenty of room for a stream of family and friends to drop by, but small enough to be cosy. The garden was big and well established, but still had plenty of scope for Mum to make it her own. There was bush and wildlife all about, the neighbourhood was friendly and safe, and it was only a few minutes' drive from where I was living.

She moved in at the start of 1996 and from the very beginning revelled in her new home, and the new life she built there. Like many women of her generation she had never had a place that was just hers. She'd gone straight from her parents' home to life with Bob (unconventionally for her day, she more or less lived with him before they were married in order to allow him to still qualify for his Rhodes Scholarship, which required him to be single), and then she'd had a house full of kids, but she'd never had a place that was solely hers. I still smile when I think about how truly happy she was to be on her own. She rang me late in the afternoon on the first day she moved in and said, 'I've never been happier anywhere! I can do what I want when I want. I can put music on when I like.

I'll be able to put the light on to read in the middle of the night. I can cook when I want, if I want. It's terrific!' There were still sometimes feelings of sadness and anger but this was the beginning of a real renaissance in Mum's life. It was all new, and this seemed to revitalise her. She felt nurtured by her environment and she adored it. Even though it had come about in a manner no-one would wish, she found herself right where she wanted to be. More and more when she talked about it she'd say, 'I'm so glad I'm on my own. This is wonderful. I feel lucky!'

Having felt such concern for Mum and for how life would be for her after the split, I felt immeasurable relief and pleasure to see her launching so happily into this new life. Some opportunities are unwelcome when they arrive on our doorstep, but finish up as blessings in disguise and I started to feel that this was one of them. It was different from what she'd had in mind when she wrote her autobiography, but it had become her own life, really.

DURING THE FIRST YEAR OR two in her new house Mum was bubbling with enjoyment of life and plans for the future. 'In my next phase . . .' has long been one of her characteristic phrases, and we started hearing it more frequently as she reflected broadly on how she wanted to live, the things she wanted to do. The tone of these reflections was, in this period, very upbeat – expansive, forward-looking, and rich with the possibilities she envisaged, while at the same time treasuring simple times at home. She talked about maybe travelling overseas, to London to see one friend or perhaps to see others in New York. She talked about how she'd like to play more golf. There were, as ever, numerous causes and community activities she wanted to get more involved in. She talked about writing more books. (After *My Own Life* she published two other books: *A Little Bit of Magic: Thoughts for Women*, which came out in 1994 and *Reflections on Marriage*, an anthology which she selected and introduced, which came out in 1996.) She occasionally joked about writing a new autobiography, with a seriously revised ending!

When Mum first moved in she had fun making the place her own. She renovated a bit of this and painted a bit of that and worked energetically in the garden. She took down a couple of small, clipped trees that looked 'too formal' – although she generally dislikes heavy-handed gardening, preferring to work around what is already in place, she could not get comfortable with them. 'I'm afraid they're just not me,' she declared when I turned up one day to find them gone. Instead she planted a variety of natives, plenty of azaleas, and started to make it her own space. The garden has always been alive with tales for Mum. Every plant has its own story, about the friend who gave it to her, or the place she found it, and they all have their own personalities. One of our oldest enjoyments to sit in the garden together and talk about them as if we're discussing some bizarre extended family. It's a live soap opera.

She got to know the area by taking long walks – keeping an eye on the state of the bush and gardens along the way. She quickly became friendly with the warm and welcoming people in her street. People have asked me if she found it difficult to return to a 'normal suburban life', but if you know Mum, that seems an odd question. From the beginning, she enjoyed the relaxed sense of neighbourhood, and felt at home in it. She still does. Even though she's well known, Mum has never had tickets on herself. People pick up their cue from her and there is never any air of 'celebrity' about her, so just as always it was easy for her to get to know new people. She saw friends often and went to concerts. She spent a lot of time with her grandchildren. Life was good.

I still feel thankful for this period when Mum put down her roots. She was still well enough to really settle in deeply and now, even though things have changed for her, she has made it clear that she has no intention of uprooting again.

At the same time she was building a new personal life, she was actively creating a new phase of her working and public life. At the beginning of 1997 she took on the role of Chair of the New South Wales Heritage Council in addition to her other existing work, including being on the board of the Australian Children's Television Foundation, her patronage of WWF Australia, and several commercial endorsements. (She was faced, for the first time in many years, with the need to earn income on her own.) In October that year she travelled to Canberra for the creation of the Sea of Hands at

Parliament House. The Sea of Hands was a wonderful physical representation of the signatures gathered by Australians for Native Title and Reconciliation (ANTaR) in support of Indigenous people and their rights, particularly to Native Title. It was a knee-high forest of plastic hands in the colours of the Aboriginal and Torres Strait Islander flags, each one bearing a signature of a supporter. The Canberra installation was the first, and the Hands then travelled around Australia, with more being added all the time.

The cause of justice and fair dealing for Indigenous people had long been dear to Mum's heart, so she was thrilled to be there for this wonderful event that movingly represented so much commitment and hope for a better Australia. There is a picture that I treasure of her and her friend Aboriginal leader Lowitja O'Donoghue, with their arms around one another; two old ladies with faces like happy kids in front of all these coloured hands.

The following month the National Trust released its list of Australia's '100 Living National Treasures'. This was a clever exercise that raised awareness of the Trust and its work. People were invited to write in to nominate those they thought should be on the list and the 'voting' was open for three months. Almost 10,000 people responded, and Mum was one of those who made the Top 100 list. It was a nice mark of recognition, but she didn't take it too seriously. The family, however, teased her mercilessly about it: 'But you can't say that, you're a Living National Treasure!'

On Australia Day 1998, Mum helped launch the Sorry Books in Sydney. These were books created by ANTaR in which Australians could express their sorrow for the way Indigenous people had been treated, either by simply signing their name or adding a personal message to their signature. No-one foresaw the huge response they would generate: almost immediately the reprinting began, and eventually there were 1000 books circulated around the country. It is believed that the books, which were ceremonially handed to Indigenous leaders that year on 26 May, National Sorry Day, contain almost one million signatures. Again, the success of this project was something that filled Mum with pride for the future of the country she loves. (While recognising our flaws as a nation, she is an unabashed patriot . 'Best country in the world!', she'll say with a smile.)

Just a few days later, on 2 February, she was off to Canberra again, this time to participate in the Constitutional Convention, a body set up to canvass views across the spectrum on the issue of Australia becoming a republic and to create a model on which the nation could vote in a referendum. Mum had lent her name to the push for change by supporting the Australian Republican Movement (ARM). But, being terminally modest as she is, she was totally surprised when she romped home as one of the 27 elected candidates who would represent ARM at the convention. (The election was held nationally from the electoral rolls, but wasn't compulsory. More than 5.6 million people voted, and there were

76 delegates appointed by parliament as well as 76 who were elected.)

The Con Con, as it was nicknamed, was another important national event in which her participation was welcomed. Hers was in one way a high-profile role: among other things she gave one of the ARM's three opening day speeches, and she did it well. But already there were changes in Mum's memory that were starting to concern me and the others closest to her. And they were concerning Mum herself, too. By this stage I was feeling anxious and protective enough to make sure I went to Canberra with her for the first day, although I also made sure that she didn't think it was 'hand-holding', but rather support for a demanding task. Still, going along with her like that because I was concerned about how she'd manage was not something I'd have done previously.

The life she developed for herself in those two years when she was newly independent was one she relished. But she had too little time to enjoy it to the full.

## CHAPTER 3

# A Creeping Thing

ONE OF THE CHALLENGES in writing this book has been trying to look back and identify when the first symptoms of Mum's Alzheimer's were emerging. To tease out a narrative from any non-linear jumble of remembered facts, feelings, events and nuances, one that is sufficiently 'true' and accurate to be a fair and useful reflection, is confounding enough. It's tricky for a whole lot of reasons. Memory is a fallible thing at the best of times: our memories are subjective and selective by nature. Looking back brings its own distortions; how we remember something, now, is inevitably shaded by the changes wrought in us over time, often by the very process we are seeking to unravel. Even more so when it comes to something as emotionally charged as this. As well, the early symptoms of Alzheimer's disease are so amorphous and gradual, so open to other interpretations, that there is no 'starting point'. It's only when there is a definitive pattern that you can say this is obviously *something* that needs to be investigated further. But patterns, by definition, only make themselves obvious over time. I think the philosopher Soren Kierkegaard nailed it when he said that life can only be understood backwards, but it has to be lived forwards. There is never a point in the early progression of a condition like Alzheimer's where you see something and say to yourself, 'Ah, now I am noticing the first of what will turn out to be a pattern of symptoms.' It just doesn't happen like that!

In my experience what does happen is that there are probably a few things going on that you don't perceive as 'problems', or not as related problems anyway. Maybe you start to notice them on a subconscious level; maybe you have a niggling feeling that you mostly ignore. Then perhaps a passing thought becomes a regular thought and gels into a perception that you start to explore. Perhaps you start to actively look at the person's behaviour and see how they're going about things, and measure that against how they did the same thing a few months or a year or two beforehand. You might toy with various possible explanations, then start to crystallise a growing sense that there is 'something' happening here that can't be easily explained away. You start to wonder what you could do to help you understand, to 'make sense' of it. You wonder whether you even want to, whether you 'should'. In all this, either consciously or not, you are seeking an appropriate balance, trying to avoid becoming either unduly alarmist or dangerously complacent. And you are keenly aware that it's not your life this is about, it's someone else's. When is it 'your business'? What should you assume some responsibility for, and what should you leave be?

It's not like a baby being born or someone having a stroke, where things change enormously and clearly in a very short time. The way Alzheimer's develops in the brain is just like the way it develops in the lives of those affected by it – it's a creeping thing.

(I feel strongly that we need to recognise this because I've found that the notion that the presence of Alzheimer's wasn't spotted early enough is one that can hit carers badly. People will sometimes torture themselves thinking, 'Oh, I should've seen . . .' or 'I should've known . . .', despairing about why at the time a particular thing happened they didn't understand that it meant X or Y. As if knowing could have changed things.

I understand this well because I've been through it myself. But I know it's a downward spiral that only leads to useless guilt and an unwarranted sense that you've failed the person. Family and friends, companions and carers – whatever term you choose – need so much strength to get through what needs to be done, and to help the person with Alzheimer's live the best life they can, that these negative thoughts and feelings are merely disabling and counterproductive.)

There were also complicating factors in Mum's particular case that obscured the picture. As early as 1993 she had been concerned about her memory not being as reliable as usual. It was only a year or so since she'd had the pituitary tumour diagnosed and surgically removed. So when she sought medical advice about her memory problems, she was told that what she was experiencing was completely in keeping with the physical trauma she'd had to her brain and the general after-effects of the surgery. In fact, dementia was specifically excluded.

The emotional stress of the marriage break-up was taken into account. There was also the factor of her thyroid function, which had been affected by the pituitary problems. She was on thyroid medications, which took quite a while to adjust and re-adjust, and thyroid problems can be associated with memory difficulties and some other symptoms she was experiencing. So whatever day-to-day problems she had were seen as being consistent with all the physical and emotional strain she had been under.

We were given very similar reassurances by other doctors, separately and together, on those occasions when we asked about memory problems in the general context of Mum's ongoing medical check-ups. I certainly have no misgivings looking back on this advice, although subsequently we realised that perhaps some of those early problems might have been symptoms of the onset of Alzheimer's. But the practical effect of having received these reassurances was that we weren't looking for further explanation. That's why I didn't worry about it when, for instance, around 1997 she started to lose her house keys and I would have to pop over to let her in and find them. Yes, we thought to ourselves, Mum's memory has got a bit less reliable, and that's frustrating, but it's no big deal. Mum's not prone to worrying about herself and, perhaps taking my lead from her in those days, neither was I.

~

THERE WERE OTHER THINGS happening as well, but again they seemed to be nothing to worry about, just changes that were happening in the way Mum went about things. You become aware that changes are happening and you adjust to that as you would with a person who has, say, progressive arthritis that gradually limits their capacity. We needed to make slight adjustments day by day to the way we'd previously done things, but life is full of adjusting to change so we mostly just got on with it. Also, you have no 'norm' against which to measure changes. It might sound silly to say, but Mum had never gotten old before, so little things that were happening seemed, at first, to simply be the combined effects of stresses and ageing.

Mum's friend Wendy McCarthy said something to me recently about having always thought of Hazel as a 'young soul' – a person who had such an ongoing enthusiasm and willingness to embrace new challenges and adapt to change that you somehow didn't think of her as getting old. It reminded me of a moment of surprise I had one day during this period when I caught myself thinking, 'Oh, Mum's ageing. She's starting to "get old". I wonder what that will be like.' I realise it might seem odd given that she was already in her late 60s (I even laughed at myself at the time), but I suppose it reflects the fact that in no way was Mum planning on winding down her interest and participation in life, and it didn't really occur to me that she would be at all inclined to. When this did start to happen to some degree, it felt out of character. But as we know now, it was the disease making itself felt, not ageing per se. I strongly believe, although I'll never know for sure, that Mum's range of activity and interests would have remained broad and dynamic, unlimited by age, if she had not been 'betrayed by her brain', as I have heard her put it.

One of the areas where small gradual changes were needed was the way her personal assistant, Prue Watson, and I went through Mum's office correspondence with her. (I hadn't quite realised until I started working for her officially, in early 1995, just how much correspondence Mum received.) The mailbag was large and there were plenty of phone and fax requests every week. Our practice was to dismiss the obvious rubbish, do any necessary research, then sit down with Mum and run through the rest, giving her the letter or print-out to read, finding out what she wanted to do about it, and then undertaking the appropriate follow-up. But gradually from about 1998, Prue and I realised this was no longer working so well. We saw that when she read the material through she was sometimes missing pertinent facts or getting bits of it wrong. She wasn't consistently absorbing every detail as astutely as she previously had. So we began to do more pre-reading and interpreting of the material Mum had in front of her.

She would also sometimes say, 'We don't need to do this one now. I want to take it home and think about it.' She had often done this as a way of dealing with the workload, but we started to realise now that sometimes she wasn't quite grasping the details, and was coming up with a way to give herself more time. But then increasingly she'd forget to think about it and we'd end up having to revisit the issue, sometimes repeatedly. My responses are different now but I have to admit that at the time I often found this process frustrating.

Recognition, understanding, adaptation and acceptance are keywords for family and friends of people with Alzheimer's, but they are all things that evolve gradually and tend to happen fully only when you realise there is 'a problem'. Before that, when you simply seem to be dealing with someone who is just not paying attention when they need to or seems to be stubbornly or argumentatively repeating themselves, then of course it is sometimes irritating. I am not by nature a patient person (just ask my kids!), so sometimes when the Hazel I knew to be sharp as a tack and extremely competent at managing competing demands was stalling or apparently disinclined to focus on the task at hand I would say, 'Well, come on, we've dealt with this before,' or 'I mentioned that last week.' When you think about it, that's an absurd reaction – I mean, how does it change anything? – but it is one that most of us will have at some point in those circumstances.

Of course, it just makes it harder for the person. They're not doing it to be difficult, so saying things like that doesn't help. And if they're being cagey or defensive because they feel that something isn't quite working, then you're just going to make it worse. But this is now, that was then.

The frustration certainly wasn't a one-way street. Mum found the going a bit tough at times too, despite our best intentions. The more it became clear to me that she needed increasing support, the less I reacted when she was vague or forgetful. Instead, both Prue and I would simply provide her with more context, more explanation. When it came to going through the more complex requests she received, I would say, 'Well, I think the pros or cons of this are . . .' or 'This connects to something else you're doing in this way . . .' or whatever was appropriate. Mum was alternately grateful for this and resentful and resistant. And sometimes she would say very snappishly, 'Stop treating me like an idiot,' and I'd know that I'd started sounding patronising. It was a difficult balance and there was sometimes a kind of tetchiness that rarely happens now.

I found myself increasingly thinking about the importance of giving Mum the extra support she clearly needed without impinging on either her real or perceived independence. Prue felt just the same; at first we didn't even need to talk about how things were changing. We were aligned in our commitment to leaving the decision-making with Mum, even though we needed to manage the process more and more as time went on. It was always important that as Mum became less competent to make decisions independently, the results were still essentially her judgements, reflecting her own values and inclinations. Although we did not initially articulate it to one another, I understood that, like me, Prue believed it was crucial to be scrupulous about not manipulating Mum's choices.

Mum's decision-making has always been a collegiate process. That had been the case throughout her life and it was formalised in the Canberra years with advisers whose views she absorbed along the way to coming to her own opinion. So when we started to provide more context for the decisions she was making about work and public life, that process was very familiar to her. Mum was still *determining* her own choices, but with more explicit information from us about what the implications were. In this informative role, we made sure we just gave the context and didn't push a point of view, unless she asked for one. Sometimes that meant we'd have a situation where, for example, she'd be reviewing one of her upcoming speeches and I'd think she might've got something slightly wrong. But instead of saying, 'That's not right,' I learned to say, 'Is that the best way to do it?' Then she'd take another look. Sometimes she'd change it, but other times she'd say, 'Yes, it's fine as it is.' And if she did, that was the end of it – we were there to support her, not to start railroading.

I was out walking one day when I realised that what was going on with Mum was like a reverse of the developmental curve that starts in childhood. When you raise children you want them to become progressively more independent, competent and responsible for themselves. You support them in developing their own views, their ability to make skilled evaluations of the choices they face. As they do, you incrementally relinquish the reins of parental input and practical care. There will be some occasions, some attempts they make, when you think they're probably not quite up to whatever it is they're trying to do, but okay, fine, you tell yourself, it's part of the trip. This day, out walking, I was thinking about a conversation I'd had with Mum about doing her Christmas card list. She was getting a bit mixed up about who some of the people on it were. I thought Prue and I should look over the list for her to make sure it was all as it should be, but Mum refused, saying, 'No, I've always done this. I'll get it done.' At that stage our daughter, Sophie, was entering adolescence and becoming vigorous in her determination to set her own path. And as parents do, we were working out as we went along how best to support her. It suddenly hit me that at the same time I was dealing with this development in reverse, with the decreasing capacity of my mother.

It really struck me that in a sense it's just the cycle of life. And that realisation helped bring a measure of acceptance. It took some of the distress and concern and anxiety out of it. I thought, well, that's just what happens. It's simply the rhythm of things – to be upset seems a bit silly. They say that children can become their parents' parents at some point and this was an acceptance of the truth of that in a way. And it helped me to articulate to myself the central challenge for me. Mum wasn't moving into increasing competence; instead, the reverse was happening, but she still had the *perception* of her own full competence, and as strong an inclination as ever to be responsible for herself and make her own decisions. So how could I deal with the growing mismatch between Mum's complete determination to do this and do that, with her decreasing ability to handle things she'd once done with ease?

As a parent you might argue with a young teenager, saying, 'No, actually I don't think you're ready to go to a party till four in the morning with no parents and boys five years older than yourself,' despite them being determined to go. And there is always (well, maybe!) the fallback of parental 'discipline' when reason fails. In other words there is some sense (probably not fully shared by the teenager and quite possibly fraught in practice) that as a parent you are entitled at times to impose your judgement. At least when their welfare is at stake. But the other end of the curve has a different dynamic and different tensions. With your own parent who is understandably determined to do things the way they always have done, you may feel like saying, 'You're not quite up to it.' But you're their kid. It's not your job to tell them not to do it, and there is, of course, no sense of 'authority', or of greater accumulated wisdom to invoke – quite the reverse, in fact. And if you feel like I do about my mother you have massive respect that they're determined to keep as much control as possible of their own life. You don't *want* to interfere.

That realisation drove me in supporting Mum, and sometimes perhaps I supported her even past the point where she was truly competent to do a particular thing. But if she thought she was up to it, or even if I could tell she secretly feared that maybe she wasn't anymore, but she was damned well going to give it her best shot and retain that sense of independence, then I was not about to say, 'No, you can't.' I just couldn't do that to her.

CHAPTER 4

# The Messy Continuum

THERE WERE ABOUT THREE and a half years between the Constitutional Convention and Mum's official diagnosis with Alzheimer's disease, and over this period it became obvious there was a specific problem. Things were becoming frayed. Various tasks became harder and harder for Mum to manage on her own, yet her awareness of that fact was diminishing. By the time of the diagnosis there was a pattern of what turned out to be symptoms, although we didn't know their medical significance when they first appeared.

In October 1998 Mum campaigned for the ALP in the Federal election. It was something she'd done numerous times before. In March 1996 she'd visited 12 different electorates in three states and two and a half years later her schedule was even more demanding: 15 electorates spread throughout Queeensland, New South Wales, Victoria, South Australia and

Western Australia. In each one she would make several public and media appearances with the local candidate, speaking at functions or doing shopping centre walk-throughs. It was hard for her and I noticed how tired she was after these trips, but it didn't seem too strange; campaigning had always been an exhausting task, though one she embraced with enthusiasm.

The memory problems were getting worse. This still bugged Mum, but because of previous reassurances she'd received from doctors (and perhaps a degree of subliminal fear), she expressed no concern that it might indicate a more significant, progressive problem. We had a few funny episodes hunting around the local shopping centre with her when she couldn't remember where she'd parked the car. And keys became a problem. She was losing them more frequently, so we hid a key outside her house and for a time that worked really well – while she remembered where the key was hidden. Finding her way around was also no longer going so smoothly. Mum had never had a great sense of direction anyhow. But she was getting worse at driving to unfamiliar places and then, eventually, even to familiar ones. She also became more and more forgetful or vague about arrangements like ordering a taxi to take her to a concert or the airport. But at the same time, she didn't realise she was being vague. Increasingly she thought, for example, she'd ordered the taxi when in fact I'd ordered it or someone else had. But when she talked about having called it, we didn't tell her she was wrong, that we'd actually done it. If it made her feel better to believe she was still on top of those sorts of things – and it was obvious that it did make her feel better – that was fine.

Her friends also seemed to adapt as needed. Previously if she was going out with a friend to a gallery, a meal or a concert, it might have been either Mum or the friend who suggested the idea and made the arrangements. Increasingly it fell to her friends to take over. But no-one really talked about it much at this stage, they just sorted things out for her and then called me or Prue and gave us the details as a back-up, to make sure it got into the diary. It seemed to be just understood that's what would happen from now on. As time went on close friends would talk to me about the changes they were noticing, but these conversations had the tone of shared observations or loving concern rather than people 'addressing a problem'. If people who I knew were good friends of Mum's talked to me about some of the changes and asked if Mum was okay, I'd be up-front with them: 'There's obviously something going on but she's seeing a doctor and she's on thyroid medication and there doesn't seem the need to do anything else at this point, and she doesn't want to. We're just letting it run how it runs for now.' If people I didn't want to open up to in that way asked 'Is Hazel all right?', I'd just say, 'Yes, she's fine.'

Day by day there were also changes in the way Mum did things she'd been doing for years. For instance, washing dishes. During the first few years after Mum moved into her own house she used to come around one or two nights a week to have dinner with Jan and me and the kids. We used to clean up together afterwards and she often washed the dishes while I dried them or vice versa. I started to notice that if she was washing, the dishes weren't cleaned properly. Or if she was drying she didn't quite know where to put things anymore. So if it was the end of a long day and I was short on patience and just wanting to get them done, I would suggest to her that we'd leave the dishes and the kids could do them later.

Sewing was another thing. Mum used to sew and knit and crochet, and in her autobiography she wrote about how much she enjoyed doing these things. She was very good at them too, and for many years made clothes for herself and us kids. But those crafts all require visual and organisational acuity, and as I now realise, she was gradually losing her acuity. So somewhere in this period she stopped sewing. I presume she found herself having more and more difficulty with it and reached the point where she just didn't attempt it anymore. But that's only my guess because she didn't talk about it. Or if she did, she would simply say something like 'Oh, I can't be bothered.' Things like that just faded gradually from the scene – you'd finally notice one day that she wasn't doing something she used to anymore. (She still has a dusty pile of 'mending I'm going to do sometime'.)

Organising medication was one task that really showed how the problem progressed over a number of years. Mum was taking several prescription drugs as a result of the pituitary problems she'd had. There was thyroid medication, a mild antidepressant to counter the hormonal changes in the levels of serotonin and so on brought about by the pituitary operation, and some nutritional supplements. At the beginning of 1998 she was handling all this herself – making sure she took the pills each day and getting the right doses morning and night. But over the next year or so things started to go awry. At first it seemed that taking daily individual doses out of the jars one by one was too complicated. So we bought two of those seven-day medication dispensers for her to use. Once a week she'd make up the morning and evening dispensers for the next seven days and away she'd go.

That worked for a while, then I noticed she wasn't getting it quite right in making them up – tablets would be in the wrong box, or some were missing or doubled up. So I started making them up for her and leaving them ready for her to take. Again, that worked for a while, but then I realised Mum was sometimes getting the morning and the evening doses mixed up. I spoke with her doctor and he adjusted her medication so she could take them all in the morning. Then I'd make up the one seven-day box and leave that for her. But then I started noticing that sometimes she'd miss a day completely. That wasn't *too* bad, it was only the odd one every now and again. I decided not to worry about it at that point because having a sense of autonomy was then very important to her. But once she started missing more days I thought something was going to have to be sorted out. Then a couple of times she took two doses on the same day without realising, and that was it, something had to be done. So I started keeping her medication, leaving it for her each day and making sure she took it. But for quite a long while Mum thought she was still doing it all herself and got very stroppy if she thought anybody else was.

I developed the habit of discreetly putting the pills on the table and hanging around to make sure they were taken. She would often think she had got them out herself. It seems a petty issue, but is a good example of the gradual adaptations we made, both practically and emotionally, to the encroachment of the disease. It represents, I suppose, the way we contrived to support a sense of autonomy that was no longer fully accurate. Emotionally, a sense of full competence and autonomy was really important to Mum's wellbeing, but it was also really important, practically, to keep her medication intake safe and reliable.

I found it difficult, within myself, to adapt to the idea that being less than fully honest may be a good thing. It ran completely counter to how things had been between us, where the mutual affection and respect was very much based in a warts-and-all sort of honesty. But it became increasingly ineffective to rely on reason based on a shared perception of the facts. As Mum's memory deteriorated, yet she bullishly went on asserting that she was still doing X or Y, argument was ineffective and distressing for us both. So I started to come to terms with the notion that in specific situations care and respect for her may best be exercised by passive, or occasionally active, deception. (And when I did resort to it, I had to be damned careful, because in her state of heightened sensitivity about herself, she could be sharp as a tack in picking up anything contrived. In which case she'd be seriously unimpressed!) Anyhow, doing it this way was the right decision at the time, although going along with her misperception about the meds would come back to bite us later.

More of a sense of her covering up for her memory loss was also setting in. By now it was something she realised was an increasing problem and she developed a range of stratagems, such as being much more assiduous about keeping her diary updated and having it always near at hand. And relying on newspapers to find out what day it was (because, of course, a diary can only be of use if you already know what the date is). That worked well for a while, as Mum gets the paper delivered daily and in the early stages she could remember if that particular issue was the paper that had come that morning. So she'd look at it and that would prompt her again that, yes, today is Tuesday. But after a while that stopped working so well. After all, once you've collected the paper and brought it inside, how do you know it's today's edition, if your recall is wonky? Over time the paper she would look at as evidence of 'today's date' would be more of a random selection. I'd go in and see her reading a paper from earlier in the week but she was assuring me, tetchily on occasion, that she knew what day of the week it was, thank you, because she had today's newspaper in front of her.

We saw that more and more she was overassertive about how well she was coping, which was probably to counter the doubts she was having. Her inner confidence was diminishing. And that more assertive behaviour had a kind of hollowness to it. I think she was trying to convince herself of things she wasn't actually convinced of: that what she was remembering was correct or that she did have a grasp of a particular conversation, when actually she was doubting herself. She was no longer so sure of her foundations.

This inner doubt and the effect it had on her self-confidence also made her less of an independent decision-maker. As I've said, the decision-making process for her had always been a collegiate one, but given the compass of her strong values she had been confident about reaching her own conclusions once she'd weighed up all the information and opinions she gathered. Now, even though she didn't say anything directly, I could tell that she was more reliant on the view of people she trusted; she was basing her decisions more on them.

There's no doubt the marriage break-up shook her confidence a lot. However she had bounced back from that very well, in large part thanks to her participation in public and community life and the positive feedback she got from people in the course of that, which boosted her feelings of relevance and contribution. This was something different. It was more evident with issues she had come to more recently, where she believed in the cause but didn't feel herself to be by any means an expert: for instance, she didn't feel confident about handling the day-to-day intricacies of the Constitutional Convention. On issues she had been steeped in for a long time, such as women's issues, Indigenous rights and children's welfare, she was more confident for longer in her own independence and judgements. Where she did feel she needed more guidance, like at the Con Con, she instinctively relied on people with whom she had previously had an alignment of judgement, so there was little risk of her making out-of-character decisions.

~

LISTING ALL THESE CHANGES in this way makes it sound as if everything were clearcut which, of course, it wasn't. The changes were all happening amid the messy continuum that is life, not in the neat stage-by-stage way they end up noted down in a medical file or on a book page. It also makes it sound as if losses of all different kinds – everything from lost keys to lost competency – were what characterised this period in Mum's life. And that's not the case. They were there in the background, which is where she was determined to keep them. She still had a robust life, even while experiencing more inner doubt and frustration and needing more support. During this time she was still contributing to public life, travelling around Australia to give speeches, fulfilling commercial contracts, including TV advertisements for Herron Pharmaceuticals, and she was enjoying time with family and friends.

In July of 1999 she gave the second John Curtin Prime Ministerial Library Anniversary Lecture in Perth. She was formally introduced by Gough Whitlam, who praised her for her contribution to Australian society and noted in passing that 'her profile today remains high and her daily schedule quite daunting'. Mum's speech had been written by my brother, Steve, after he had been briefed by Mum. It was called 'In Search of the Light on the Hill' and was a very personal but far-reaching look at Australia at the end of the 20th century and the challenges it faced. In it she argued persuasively for the importance of compassion, inclusion and fairness in Australia's future, and her speech was warmly received.

A month later Mum herself, then 70, was celebrated at a tribute dinner organised by the Australian Labor Party, of which she had been an active member for more than 50 years. The event was a fundraising dinner held at the NSW Parliament House in aid of Curtin University's Hazel Hawke Scholarship Fund. It was a wonderful event and the family gathered to share it. Steve came from Perth and Ros came with her sons, David and Paul. It was particularly moving for me to watch Ben and Sophie as they absorbed just how special their Nan was. Their childhood had been pretty 'normal', fairly removed from the detail of the extraordinary lives their grandparents had lived in Canberra. They were used to my father being talked about as having been important and achieved a lot, but it hadn't extended so much into their perception of Mum. She was simply their 'Nan', whom they adored. The evening featured a few speeches in honour of Mum as well as a tribute video put together by Network 10 which showed Mum in her PM's wife role all over the world with famous people, publicly supporting various of her causes, and in more intimate moments. During it I looked across at Ben and Sophie and I could see them really taking it in and thinking, 'Oh, *that's* who my grandmother is.' ('Wow,' said Sophie to me afterwards, 'Nan met the Queen!') It was an emotional night – a tribal celebration by Mum's friends and former colleagues that typified the warmth and heart an ALP occasion can sometimes muster.

These big public appearances certainly weren't happening as effortlessly as they once had, though, and Mum herself was now having doubts and worries about the changes that she was experiencing, but she didn't dwell on them much. She did, however, start to slowly withdraw over these years, and her increasing tiredness and lack of vitality was something that became marked. It is not an early symptom for everyone with Alzheimer's by any means, in fact it's fairly uncommon, but it was evident with Mum.

Occasionally she would say to me that she was getting frustrated with not being able to do as much as she once had, but she mostly kept the specifics to herself. She'd usually turn it into a good-natured grumble about ageing: 'Getting old, bugger it!' At other, more reflective, times she would say, 'Well, I'm getting older and I don't want to stop doing things, but I think I might slow down.' For her, that meant speaking in public once a month instead of once a week, so it's all relative.

In January 2000, the day after returning from a Buddhist meditation retreat we had attended together, we received a fax from CCF, the Christian Children's Fund, to see if Mum would go to East Timor to film some ads for a fundraising appeal they were conducting. The Indonesian military had finally pulled out of the country three months earlier, having invaded 24 years before. Throughout 1999 Indonesian-backed militia groups wrought terror on the tiny country which ended only with the arrival of a UN peacekeeping force led by Australia. East Timor was devastated by this violence and the appeals were seeking sponsorship and donations for community rebuilding projects. It was the kind of thing Mum felt strongly about and she wanted to accept. I knew that to make it work I would have to go with her – by this stage it was highly unlikely she would be able to get through it smoothly on her own.

We went at the beginning of February and were only there for three and a half days, but it was a tough trip. The conditions were hard, as was only to be expected in a place that had been through so much, and it was done in steaming, relentless, tropical heat. It was also very emotionally affecting to meet people, many of them children, who had been through so much terror and seen so much death and destruction. We visited the 'Voice of Hope' radio station, housed in the remains of the very building where some of its announcers had been imprisoned and tortured during the occupation. Dili was a burnt shell. Of course Mum had been to Third World countries in her Canberra days, but when you travel in the prime-ministerial caravan you are comfortable and insulated to some degree. That was not so much the case on this trip. She was shaken but she made it through, and was far more interested in the daunting work done by the courageous people we met than in her own small contribution.

To the wider outside world she was still, during this period, doing as good a job as ever. To those more closely involved with her it was clear she needed increased support in various ways: for instance, being met at the entrance of a large convention venue instead of navigating her own way to the appropriate spot, being prompted about the running order of an event, or being briefed much more about who was who in the meet-and-greet sections afterwards. Maybe they were starting to wonder why, but nobody said anything outright at this point. I was starting to see how difficult public participation generally was for her, and I felt some relief, tinged with sadness, when she started to talk more consistently about wanting to scale back even further. As far as I was concerned, she was under no obligation to do anything she was uncomfortable with – she had well and truly earned the right to a graceful retirement. But the reason for her increasing withdrawal was not a diminished sense of commitment or wish to contribute, but rather decreasing self-confidence in public and feeling drained by the effort it took.

I still regret the decline this has caused in her engagement with new people from all walks of life. Mum always relished the personal interactions arising from her life beyond home: meeting people, hearing their stories, sharing the laughter and grief and accomplishments of so many varied people. She drew inspiration, companionship, entertainment, and a sense of meaning from it all. In many ways it was the juice that kept her going.

In June 2001 came the announcement of the Queen's Birthday Honours, in which Mum had been awarded an Order of Australia for 'service to the community, particularly through the promotion of the reconciliation process, support for continued improvement in the quality of children's television, as a contributor to the preservation of heritage items, and involvement with environmental and wildlife preservation groups'. She was pleased and honoured to be recognised in this way. Unpretentious as she is, this kind of recognition, which comes, in a way, from the Australian people, was nevertheless very meaningful to her. (Indeed she still remembers to find her AO pin and put it on whenever she is getting dressed up to go out.)

The investiture ceremony was on 14 September at Government House in Canberra. Those events can be a little daunting, but Mum had been to so many of them in 'the Canberra years', and she knew Government House itself well. In the old days she would have breezed through it. But she was clearly disoriented this day – before I left her in the area where the 33 people being given awards of various kinds were to wait, I quietly explained what was to happen, and repeated parts to reinforce them in her memory. A wonderful man named Gordon was working at Government House at that point and we knew him from his time as manager at the Lodge. I asked him to look out for her. When Mum's name was announced she stepped into the room where the Governor-General was waiting with her AO and I could see she was momentarily uncertain what to do, despite the briefing. She started to turn the wrong way, but Gordon discreetly steered her in the right direction. You would have to have been looking closely to see that something was a little wrong, but of course I was.

I was also with her a few days later when she gave the launch speech at the inaugural dinner marking a partnership between the mining company Rio Tinto and the conservation organisation WWF, of which she was patron. I had a clear sense that night of thinking to myself, 'I don't know if Mum could do this again,' because other people had had to take care of things to a greater degree than ever before.

As she got ready to speak I could sense a lesser confidence in her. I made sure she had her notes and then it was time for her to go up to the stage. She stumbled a little bit getting up onto the podium but recovered gracefully. There was a moment, looking into the bright lights, where it seemed as if she didn't know where she was. Again she recovered – she sort of laughed at herself and turned it into a joke – then delivered a great speech, again written by Steve, about the partnership and its frogs protection project. The speech was funny and frank in turn, ranging from Mum's personal acquaintance with the 'dunny frogs' of the Kimberley to the historical conflict between mining companies and Indigenous Australians. She did a great job of delivering it and it was very well received.

But I could see and feel her diminished confidence, the greater effort it took to feel on top of things, and there was great poignancy for me in that. I knew what it had taken for her to become a public speaker in the first place. She writes about it in her autobiography – the nervousness she felt and how she overcame that. She became a wonderful speaker, capable of quietly inspiring rooms full of people. Now here she was on the other end of that curve, and she knew it too. That turned out to be the last major speech she gave.

## CHAPTER 5

# Our World Changes

MUM GAVE THE WWF/RIO TINTO speech on 19 September 2001. Four weeks earlier she'd had her assessment with neuro-psychologist Robyn Murray. Mum was upset and concerned about the memory problems she was having, and the fact that there was clearly, by now, a progressive quality to them. She was, however, understandably reluctant to recognise that her cognition in some other areas was also slipping. Over the preceding months that had led to occasional tension. I'd come to pick her up, for instance, and she'd be in a perfectly suitable outfit to go out to a concert and then she'd add a scarf that clashed horribly, which was not something she would previously have done. Or I'd come to get her to take her to a function and she'd be all dressed and ready, she thought, except that she'd be wearing casual shoes. And she couldn't see why it was necessary for her to change. Her previously sound sense of social conventions was getting wobbly. As much as possible, where it didn't matter much, I would make a mild suggestion or comment and, if she didn't take it on board I'd let it go at that. If she wore something that looked odd but she was just going for a walk, or to a family dinner, fine. But if it involved Mum being in the public eye – if it risked her dignity, by her own previous standards – then I did step in, and that's when conflict sometimes arose.

Occasionally Mum would agree to, for instance, change her outfit. But all too often it would become a tense and unpleasant exchange. She was very stroppy about any intervention. That has changed a lot now, but back then it was one of the ways in which she was maintaining her sense of independence and self-control. Even when her judgement about something was considered by everybody else to be a bit flawed, she was absolutely insistent that she was right, and she'd get quite shirty if you tried to correct her. She didn't take kindly to it at all, and it was without doubt a difficult period.

Her fierce desire for normality and independence was mostly what led me to let things go on as they were for as long as possible. I know that some other people would have intervened more and sooner; indeed there was some disagreement within the family about how 'bad' Mum was getting and what needed to happen as a result. But my view was that there were still so many things she was doing well, or well enough, and those things she wasn't handling well were generally not a big deal. With a bit of extra support she could manage. And I was learning to relax about what really mattered – if things were not up to Mum's previous standards, then so what – things change. Managing on her own as much as possible was so important to her that for a long time it seemed to me to overshadow the benefits of pursuing a medical investigation that she didn't want. During the course of 2001 that balance shifted.

Late in March there had been an incident that was worrying on a number of levels. I was going out to a meeting that evening, where Mum would know some people. I'd asked Mum if she wanted to come, and she'd said no. I'd squeezed a trip with the kids to the local shopping centre between work and the meeting, and we were sitting in the local sushi bar when Mum called. 'I don't mean to bother you, darling,' she said, 'but I've cut myself and I'm bleeding everywhere.' She sounded shaken, and it was unlike her to ring for help unless there was a real problem. So I thought I'd better nip up there immediately and see what was going on. I dropped the kids back home and raced up to Mum's. When I got there she was apologetic for having called me and also rather vague.

She had a bandaid on her hand where she'd hurt it while she was up a ladder cutting the wisteria off her roof with new, sharp secateurs. I had a look at the cut, which was on the webbing between her thumb and index finger, but the wound was clean and wasn't bleeding. It didn't seem to be more than a small cut but she was clearly bothered by it. So I asked if she'd like me to take her to the doctor's; if she'd like to come with me to the meeting, or if she'd rather I stayed at home with her. She wouldn't go to the doctor; instead she decided to come with me. Before we headed out I put a small bandage around her hand, over the bandaid, mainly to stop her thumb from moving too much.

By now she seemed quite dazed and I was mildly concerned but she was insistent she wanted to come. I thought to myself that we'd see how it went; we'd sit through the meeting and then I'd take her home. But during the evening I looked down at her hand and there was copious blood soaking through the white bandage. Mum hadn't noticed. We left the room and I looked again and saw that what had seemed like a simple cut was actually a flap of skin hiding a deeper wound. The blood wasn't bright red or spurting so I didn't panic, but there was enough to think she probably needed stitches. By this time it was quite late and her GP was long closed for the day so we went straight to a medical centre near home and got the wound stitched. The doctor gave her some Panadeine Forte on the spot and a couple extra to take home, with instructions to have them if she needed to after the first dose had worn off. I took her home and settled her into bed. She was all tucked up, happy and sleepy, so I headed home.

An hour or so later the phone rang and it was Mum again. 'I'm sorry to ring you again,' she said, 'but I've got chest pains.' I was up and out of bed and getting dressed before she finished the sentence. I asked her a couple of questions, such as: 'How long ago did they start? Are you moving around? Are you breathing okay?', just to keep her talking so I could hear how she was doing. I told her I was on my way, hung up, woke Jan while I called an ambulance. I was at Mum's in less than three minutes and she was okay in that she was able to breathe and sit up, but she was very anxious. She was trying so hard not to be, but she couldn't hide it. She described to me the chest pains and palpitations she was feeling. Then the ambulance arrived. The paramedics said they thought she was all right, that she wasn't having a heart attack, but at her age – 71 – they thought it prudent to take her to hospital for further checks, just to make sure. They put Mum in the ambulance and took her to the emergency department at Royal North Shore Hospital, and I followed.

She was taken through to Intensive Care for a series of tests, and the staff asked me to wait outside while these were done. My gut feeling was that she was okay, but I was still very much on edge. I settled myself by reading a Buddhist text I had with me. To my relief, the tests showed that it definitely wasn't a heart attack, but what had caused such physical distress in Mum wasn't clear. Her doctors came to think that it was slight shock from the cut and then the stitches, combined with overstimulation from being at a public meeting, and a reaction to an overdose of painkillers – we later realised she took the two extra tablets at home, not remembering she had already had a dose.

After hearing about the test results, I was allowed in to see her. She asked me what was happening. 'You haven't had a heart attack, but you're in hospital and while you're here the doctors want to do some further tests, just to make sure you're completely okay.' She was initially resistant: 'No, I don't want any fuss. I'm all right and nothing's wrong with me, really, I don't want any fuss.' But eventually she agreed to accept the medical advice that further tests were a responsible precaution, and was transferred to a ward where she could undergo some heart-stress checks, treadmill tests and so on, over the next couple of days. She was adamant that she didn't want me telling anyone, or creating too much concern.

The follow-up tests confirmed that her heart was fine but it was painfully obvious that she was not in good shape. Literally overnight she had dipped dramatically in her ability to understand what was happening. She was beyond forgetful; she was very confused and her memory was markedly worse than before the accident. The confusion was seemingly out of proportion to the circumstances. It also lingered, even when things should have been getting back to normal. My concern increased as the days went by without any real improvement. I thought we needed to get it checked out sooner rather than later so I called to see Mum's GP, Dr Richard Schloeffel, to talk with him about her condition. He agreed it was time to investigate what might be causing it.

After Mum was back home and feeling more settled we discussed it. She accepted, in principle, that it was a good idea to seek further advice, but her heart wasn't in it, and she resisted hurrying towards any specialist investigation. She was happy, however, to talk to Richard about it, so I thought it best to take things gently, and made an appointment for us to see him together. He talked with her about her overall wellbeing, and said that although she had obviously been coping very well with her concerns about her memory, there was enough evidence of progressive memory loss and cognition issues that he thought it advisable to investigate further. He suggested that we seek specialist advice, which is when Dr Terry Finnegan's name first came up.

While we were waiting for our appointment in his busy schedule to come around, Robyn Murray saw Mum for a neuropsychological assessment. But despite everything that had happened, and Mum's own reluctant feeling that she needed to get further medical advice about what was going on, she did not take kindly to it.

Robyn visited Mum at home and conducted a fairly standard series of tests. This included checking her verbal abilities – reading, spelling, naming and simple arithmetic; her spatial abilities; her attention and ability to focus; her learning abilities – retaining a sequence of words for up to 30 minutes; her memory, both visual and verbal; her planning and problem-solving abilities; and her intellectual functioning. There were about 12 different tests in all, including a grooved pegboard exercise, where Mum had to put the pegs in their correct holes.

To say she felt negative about all this would be a major understatement. It was not Robyn's fault – she is an immensely likable, skilled and empathetic person. I could see it wasn't so much that Mum didn't like Robyn, but rather that Robyn represented a process that she resented. I haven't heard it for a while now, but for a long time after the tests she would talk scathingly about it: 'What's wrong with these people? They wanted me to do bloody kindergarten things – put silly little pegs in fiddly little holes!' But I think underlying that reaction was a discomfort with herself, and fear, because she thought she'd do better in the tests.

Mum's test results showed that while there were many things she could still do very well, for instance her vocabulary abilities were in the 98th percentile (in other words she was in the highest three per cent of ability compared to people her age) and her verbal intellectual functioning was intact, a lot of areas showed clear problems. All aspects of her memory were impaired; her reading comprehension was seriously affected by her memory loss; tasks requiring certain kinds of attention, such as copying a series of symbols, were not easy for her; her ability to switch back and forth between tasks was not good; and her ability to make connections between things and to learn completely new tasks was also impaired.

Robyn compared her findings with those from a set of tests Mum had undergone in 1993, after her brain surgery. The 1993 test results showed that Mum had a mild weakness in verbal memory, but her visual memory, and attention, concentration, information processing and executive functioning were all intact. Robyn noted that these latest results indicated a 'significant decline in functioning'. It was clear this was not good, but what exactly did it mean?

I met with Robyn to discuss her findings. She was both professional and kind, concentrating at first on the positives. She talked about how the results showed that Mum was a very intelligent woman and that her verbal skills were still very high. But we also talked about the memory and cognition problems that were so evident and about Robyn's finding that the pattern of results was consistent with 'a cortical dementing condition'. In other words, Alzheimer's disease was a strong possibility. I felt a big reaction to that. It wasn't disbelief, but I was a long way from being able to deal with it. I didn't deny the truth of what Robyn was saying. I couldn't, given that it fitted with the problems we had been noticing for quite a while. Robyn was not 'doom and gloom' at all; she was reassuring about Mum's strengths, and about the degree to which she, and we, could develop strategies to support and prolong her independence. But still I felt I needed time to process what I'd just heard. I needed to be able to deal with it myself before I dealt with how it would hit everybody else.

A few days later, Robyn sat down with Mum to discuss the results. It was, in a way, anticlimactic. Mum just didn't seem to give it a huge amount of credence. Thinking about it afterwards, it occurred to me that perhaps it was partly emotional denial, but I think it was also that Mum didn't see Robyn in the same way she would see a senior male doctor. It's ironic because Mum is a bone-deep supporter of women and their capabilities, but her generational upbringing sometimes causes her, subconsciously, to look for a different kind of authority. Robyn had come to her house, rather than Mum going to Robyn's professional rooms, and her manner was empathetic and low-key, rather than professional and authoritative. And she'd had Mum do 'all those silly things'. So somehow what she said didn't have a solid reality to it for Mum.

Still, it might seem odd to some people that Mum was able to get up and deliver a successful speech with this hanging over her, but it makes perfect sense to me. First there was her kind of refusal to take it seriously, but beyond that is the fact that Mum is not a 'dweller'. Her view, which I share, is that there may be something raw or difficult in your life but it doesn't mean it has to occupy your attention every minute of the day if you can help it. It's best to get on with whatever it is that's required of you. If that is getting up and giving a speech, then you get up and give a speech. Life goes on. Her reaction, or lack of reaction, at this point meant that it was only when the diagnosis of Alzheimer's came from Dr Terry Finnegan that Mum was really 'hit' by the news.

For me, though, the world had rocked on its axis. It's odd, thinking about it now, how all this coincided with other changes that were happening on the world stage. The September 11 attacks happened right in the middle of this period. I can remember the shock of that: Jan and Sophie waking me to tell me what had happened, watching the early morning footage of the planes flying into the Twin Towers. In the days and weeks after the attacks there was a sense that the world had changed forever. Our small corner of it certainly had.

~

DISCUSSING ROBYN'S FINDINGS WITH her did soften me up and allow me to start absorbing the thought that there was a good chance Mum had Alzheimer's, but Terry Finnegan's confirming diagnosis was what really brought it home and made it irrevocable. And that's why I can best describe the impact of what he said as a shock but not a surprise.

In the immediate aftermath of our visit to him life felt very, well, warpy is probably the best word for it. Nothing had changed as such, but we were dealing with the traumatic impact of the word. It seemed much harder then than it does now, even though the disease has progressed so much. Dealing with the effect of diagnosis – the upset, the undeniable reality and our concerns for the future, amid coping with the rest of day-to-day life – felt like wading through wet cement. Mum dealt with it mostly by not being very 'present' much of the time. But I was feeling raw with grief. Bereft, overwhelmed by the spectre of Mum's 'living death'.

Jan, of course, was a great support. And Dad's reaction was touching. He was not surprised when I told him, but he was very, very sad. His eyes teared up. And even though he is in some ways more obviously emotional than a lot of men his age, he still had what I think of as the classic male reaction, which is, 'What can I do?' It's that coping mechanism that so many men use; of looking for something practical so they can spring into action. They find it hard to simply absorb this kind of sad or difficult news without trying to do something. Dad asked me if Mum was still reading books and when I said yes he asked, 'Would she like a signed copy of Kim's biography?' 'I'm sure she would,' I said. So he got up and rang Kim Beazley on the spot and arranged for him to send Mum a copy of his newly released biography, which Kim duly did and Mum very much enjoyed reading. It was sweet. Dad was, and continues to be, supportive of me in his own indirect, gruff sort of way.

Despite my inclination at that stage to be fiercely protective of Mum's privacy, and my own, I cautiously told a few close friends. A burden shared, etc. . . . Wendy McCarthy, who is one of Mum's closest friends and a wonderful, wise woman to whom I turn for advice and support, especially regarding Mum, was terrific. I visited her so that I could tell her what had happened. She was at her daughter's place delighting in looking after her new grandson, and she wasn't surprised either, but she was acutely sad. We had a bit of a cry together, and I thought, as she rocked the baby to sleep, about the three generations in the room and the fact that birth and death, growth and decline, joy and sadness are all part of the cycle. There was a bittersweet solace in that.

Wendy was very solicitous of how I felt and also very

practical. She assured me deeply that she would be there for Mum and for me throughout the process, whatever unfolded, and that too was a great comfort. I felt again that how you share the news and how it is received is important. That having sensible and good-hearted people with whom to share it makes a lot of difference. I started to realise that subconsciously I was steering away from telling some people and towards telling others, and it wasn't necessarily about who would care the most or the least. The people I wanted to tell were the ones I instinctively knew would be able to empathise, to 'be present' to what I was telling them; in other words to listen and share without adding a lot of unnecessary angst or drama. I find unnecessary dramatics tiresome, especially when I'm feeling vulnerable. Which is a funny thing, given that I am part of a family with a well-developed capacity for the dramatic!

I'm sure it's not healthy to suppress grief or other strong emotions, or to be embarrassed about expressing them, but it seems to me to be equally unhelpful to exacerbate them by persistently magnifying the negative. People whose reaction was to rail against fate, saying 'This is wrong!' or 'But she doesn't deserve this!', were just adding petrol to the fire of my own grief. What I needed, and found solace in, was compassion and a calm recognition that what was happening was tough and was sad. I simply wasn't ready to handle other people's grief and turbulence. I was too raw. I have heard people who have had a loved one die say that one of the things they find very hard to deal with is having to take care of other people's reactions while they're still dealing with their own grief. It's not that other people aren't entitled to grieve in their own way, on the contrary; but when you are at your most vulnerable, as I was then, some people are easier to be with than others.

Some days were better than others, too. One morning very soon after the diagnosis I was driving in to the city to go to a meeting about some project consultancy work that might be coming up, on which I'd be collaborating with two women, one of whom I knew slightly and the other not at all. I was listening to a compilation CD I'd made of songs I enjoyed listening to while driving. My mascara never made it to the meeting. First I noticed a line from a Dylan song – 'You can't win with a losing hand'. That set me off. Then Tina Turner's *Simply the Best* (a number that had been hijacked to advertise rugby league at one point) reminded me of Sogyal Rinpoche, a Tibetan lama and teacher, who's a deep source of inspiration and comfort and all sorts of other good things in my life – for me, he's simply the best. So it's a song I've listened to many times. But all of a sudden I heard, really heard for the first time, the line 'Take my heart and make it stronger'. And I burst into more tears.

I was driving along with tears streaming down my face because the words seemed to be aimed straight at me. What was happening with Mum was like an assault on my heart. And when life deals out these things you sometimes don't know how you're going to handle it. Are you going to be strong enough to really support those you love? It can seem so daunting, all of it. But at the same time, while your heart is being torn there is a sense that hopefully, through it all, your heart can become bigger and stronger, that you can grow to meet the challenge. And you need help to make that so. You need help and faith and support and other people's love, and then maybe you'll be able to see it through.

There I was, driving, weeping, praying, singing, thinking all these things when there was a sudden bang and a big wobble. A bad car noise. A flat tyre. It could hardly have happened in a worse place. I was on the freeway approaching the Sydney Harbour Bridge. Fortunately there was a dead spot out of the flow of traffic that I was able to pull into. But I'd never changed a tyre on this particular car before and I didn't even know where the tools were. Just a moment before I'd been hoping that *maybe* there was enough love and strength in me and in the world ultimately to deal with anything pretty much, but I really had not been envisaging a tyre change on an expressway! I felt utterly done in, and thought, 'I'm not up to this right now. I can't cope.' But what was I going to do, throw up my hands in despair and give up? The dramatics I was feeling started to seem rather absurd – a bit of a soap opera, really. For a moment I wanted desperately to be 'rescued', but helplessness was not much use on a speeding freeway. It all somehow seemed very symbolic. This new glitch had to be dealt with, it wasn't the end of the world, and it was up to me to do it. So I got on with it: found the manual, the tool kit, the jack, changed the tyre and got in to my meeting a little late.

But by the time I arrived I was feeling pretty damned thin at the edges. It was supposed to be a project consultation meeting but the first half-hour ended up being me blubbering and telling these two women about Mum. I think that was the first time I blurted it out to people outside immediate family or very close friends. And I found great solace in the sharing of it and the comfort they gave me in return. The capacity to simply be present to another person's experience is magic. But it can be hard for most of us, especially when that experience is uncomfortable or threatening or challenging or painful. We want to come up with the 'right' response that will make everything better, but sometimes we can't – some things cannot be 'fixed'. In fact, as these two good-hearted people, who were virtually strangers when I walked in the door, demonstrated, when you're fully present for another person then whatever happens is right. There is no formula; whatever happens is okay and everyone concerned is the better for it.

CHAPTER 6

# The Right to Self-determination

LIVING WITH THE IMPACT of the diagnosis in the months that followed was strange. We felt strong underlying grief and concern, but at the same time it was oddly irrelevant to daily life. At various points people gave us books and pamphlets about the disease and how it worked, and how people lived with it. Mainly they would give this material to me, but some of it they gave to Mum directly. Having always been someone who gathered information on whatever it was she was involved in, on this she mostly just didn't want to know. Her initial self-protective forgetting in the days after the diagnosis evolved into a general vagueness on the topic most of the time. We didn't refer to it all that much. It came up, of course, but I didn't press it. And then even when it did become a bit more of a reality for her, and she occasionally told someone – 'Oh, I've got Alzheimer's, you know' – we still didn't talk about it day in day out.

It's not really the sort of thing you can keep talking about all the time anyhow. What are you going to say? In a sense it does sound slightly ridiculous now to look back and say we'd been given this life-affecting news, however it didn't really dominate the conversation. But on the other hand the rest of life didn't stop. All of us, including Mum, were still busy with the range of our day-to-day activities. And she was no less capable the day after the diagnosis than she had been the day before. The fact that we knew Mum had Alzheimer's was now part of the mix, but it didn't bring everything else to a grinding halt.

In fact it was because life was rolling on that we had to start talking more explicitly about the disease and the changes it was bringing. We were still dealing with running a public life: Mum had some commercial contracts that she was fulfilling and although she gave no more major speeches she was still making some public appearances to support pet causes. There were also her ongoing roles as chair of the NSW Heritage Council and board member of the Australian Children's Television Foundation. Although these things were winding down, there was still considerable work to be done and she needed more and more support to manage her commitments, and her social life too. But her own knowledge that she had Alzheimer's didn't always make this increasing support easy to accept. She was often frustrated and stroppy during this time. Sometimes with Prue and me, as we went with her through her diary and talked through the requests that were coming in, but often with herself. Sometimes she was self-deprecating about it: 'Oh, silly old me!', but essentially she resented having lost her capacity to do things to her own high standards without needing 'hand-holding'.

It occasionally made our relationship fractious. There were, of course, lots of good times as well – family dinners, spending time in the garden together, concerts. All the things that we had always enjoyed together. But there was an undercurrent of frustration and anger that sometimes flared up. I felt that I understood it – Mum was dealing with her own irritations, fear and sorrow. But it was still hard to cope when it manifested as an aggressive assertion of her own capacity – a capacity she actually no longer fully had. I was starting to feel a little like Alice in Wonderland.

Her ability to drive was one good example. Even before the diagnosis she had been having more trouble with driving, or more specifically with navigating her way around. She was getting lost more frequently. At first it was just in relatively unfamiliar areas, but by late 2001 she was losing her way even in places she had been to before. She dealt with this in her own way, by mostly limiting her driving to the local area – it was pretty much restricted to her own suburb, the neighbouring one where my family then lived, and two of the shopping centres nearby. I remember a couple of funny conversations when she called me on her mobile from the car and, street directory in front of me, I would attempt to guide her out of some unfamiliar spot she found herself in. And yet whenever I tried to bring up the topic of her driving, specifically that I was worried it was no longer such a great idea, she would flatly refuse to consider stopping altogether. And this was even the case immediately after the diagnosis. (Mum famously said in her *Australian Story* program that she was forced to give up her licence because of the diagnosis – that this was simply the law. That's not correct; it's a confusion that Mum picked up somewhere along the way. However Alzheimer's Australia does recommend that driving cease fairly early on in the disease.) I made sure that occasionally, when we were going somewhere together, we went in Mum's car and she drove, so that I could get a direct 'take' on whether her driving skills had deteriorated to a point where she was unsafe to herself or others. Although she was a more hesitant driver than previously, and I could see the time approaching when driving would no longer be responsible, I felt she was still coping okay, so opted not to press the issue too forcefully.

In the end it took a combination of some good (bad) luck and an appeal to Mum's altruism to get through to her. A friend of the family had borrowed her car and had an accident in which the car was written off (the friend was fine). Seeing the opportunity to come at the issue from a different angle, Jan and I decided that instead of getting a replacement car we would arrange to take the insurance payout and add it to

Mum's finances. When she suggested that she should get another car, we focused on the risks to other people on the road. That worked. Up until that point her whole response had been that we were being silly and intrusive to suggest she shouldn't drive anymore. It's odd in one way, because she's not wilfully irresponsible or self-aggrandising in her judgements of herself. On the contrary, she's terminally modest. But, during this period, her assertion of her own capacity and independence was increasing as her actual capacity was decreasing. And that dissonance is not just about Mum's personality or her way of coping, it's also a function of the disease. Some of Mum's behaviour during this period was in fact 'out of character', inconsistent with her personality up till then. By this stage, I had come to a fuller understanding of the ways in which both a person's cognitive perceptions, and self-perception, are distorted by the disease. Learning this is one thing; integrating it with your knowledge of a person, and how you interact with them, is a slower process, one that takes time, trial and, sometimes, error.

Fighting the driving battle would have been very hard indeed if Mum's sense of responsibility weren't so deeply ingrained. She thought we were overreacting and being a bit foolish, but if there was any chance we were right about her possibly endangering other people then that was a chance she would not take. Although she does still tell anyone who asks that 'they won't let me drive' with a firm glare that implies that 'they' are wrong, and she is merely tolerating misguided intervention. 'Anyhow', she sniffs, 'it's not a problem. I got used to it quickly, and I like walking. It's good for me.'

As time passed conversations with Mum and about Mum became more focused on the practical implications. Jan and I talked a lot with each other and with Mum about what we needed to do to ensure that her finances were in order, and to take care of all that we could in this early stage to make sure that she would have everything she needed further down the track. This in itself was not new – well before the obvious onset of the disease, she had made it very clear that she wanted us to hold the responsibility, with her and for her, for various practical, medical and financial aspects of her life. She had made her will, given Jan her Power of Attorney, and discussed various hypothetical future scenarios with us. Prue and I talked with Mum about what she wanted to do in terms of all the other aspects of her work and life. She still had capacity in terms of deciding how she wanted things to be – to articulate guidelines that we could follow as her capacity diminished. I felt strongly about this, and Prue shared my feelings. It was very important to us that she, as much as possible, set the terms now for her life in the future.

Looking at Mum's life, her commitment to people's right to self-determination shines out to me through the decades. When I think about how she raised me and Ros and Steve, she was very open and in a sense very permissive, but not at all lackadaisical or uncaring. She was committed and imaginative in supporting us to form our own views and opinions, to explore the world and to become self-determining, self-responsible people. And she was ahead of her time in that sense. Her embrace of the women's movement and feminism was premised on the right of women to self-determine; this same attitude underlies her support for Aboriginal people and land rights. It informed the work she did in welfare – her passionate belief in helping people to determine their own lives was the reason she chose to focus on that area, first as a volunteer with the Brotherhood of St Laurence. Then, after she had returned to study in her fifties and qualified with a diploma, as a worker there.

That sense of respect for all people, and her belief that everyone should have the means and opportunity to determine their own lives, is bone-deep in my mother. And she has well and truly passed those values on in her work. As the wheel turns, I can see these values reflected in my own life, and specifically in how I seek to support Mum herself. It's not always easy to achieve, but Mum has shown me by example that it is the right thing to aim for.

So how could I do anything other than try my hardest to help Mum to maintain her independence, both real and perceived as long as possible? Part of that, for me, was getting her explicit instructions early on, when she was clearer, so that even as her capacity to shape her own life decreases I can make sure that what is done on her behalf is, as far as possible, as she would have wanted to do it herself. Mum has always wanted to be her own person, and I believe to honour that is really the only decent thing to do.

This attitude seems to me to be the strongest argument for advocating the value of early diagnosis of Alzheimer's. Mum had, in fact, put a lot in place before her dementia became apparent, but this is not always the case. And it seems to me to be important that the person with the disease not be deprived of the opportunity to make choices, as far as possible, about their own future while they still meaningfully can. As medical understanding of Alzheimer's slowly improves, and more useful medications become available, there is an increasing practical value in seeking diagnosis and medical care, too. There is also increasing value in the work, for instance, of Alzheimer's Australia with programs such as 'Living with Memory Loss', which supports people with the disease, and their 'carers', in maintaining a satisfying and self-determining life for as long as possible. So there are major positives that can come from diagnosis. Yes, it brings with it a great deal of sorrow and often fear and dread, but it can also be the best opportunity for the person with the disease to set their own terms, as much as possible, for the way the rest of their life will unfold. Apart from simple issues of respect, this seems to me to be an important reason for working towards destigmatising Alzheimer's – to combat fear and dread with information and understanding. To talk about, and improve, what *can* be done, while not taking lightly the sadness about what, as yet, can't be changed.

One thing that I was already very clear about was Mum's desire not to be 'kept alive' for the sake of it. That long predated her Alzheimer's. While I was growing up, both my parents were always very practical and clear-eyed about death. They weren't sentimental about it and they weren't dramatic. Their view was simply that we all die and it's pointless to worry about the inevitable. I remember talking with Dad years ago, after a threat was made on his life, and supposedly ours, that police were taking seriously. There was a 24-hour watch on the house, and at one stage we kids spent a week, with police escort, at a farm out of town. But there was no atmosphere of alarm at all from Mum or Dad, and I remember being curious about their apparent unconcern. Dad just said that he supposed he was obliged to take the police concerns seriously, but he couldn't get excited about it, and was not in the least influenced to change what he was doing. 'It gives me the shits that it affects you kids, but as for me – you go when you go.'

I'm not suggesting that either of them have reached an exalted state of enlightenment or they might not get upset about their own death if it was imminent, but they've never entertained a sense of fear or avoidance about it. They are very realistic and pragmatic, both of them, about a lot of things, including death. I think always what horrified Mum much more than dying was the idea of losing her self-determination – losing herself, in effect. She said to me years ago that she did not want to be kept alive if that meant becoming a 'vegetable'. That is such an awful image, but it is so prevalent. Even when it's unspoken the echoes of it seem to persist in almost every conversation about dementia and how that might end. For Mum that state meant a time when she was insensible to her surroundings and unable to do anything for herself. 'No use to myself or anybody else,' is how she put it.

Now here she was, having been diagnosed with a disease that has been described as the death of self. An attack on the brain that erodes so much of what makes you you. But of course, nothing is ever quite the way you think it will be. Yes, Mum feared loss of self more than death, and now she had a disease that may well lead her to exactly that fate, but in real life it's not like all of a sudden you've got Alzheimer's and then you're sitting in a nursing home, insensible. It's a gradual process, an erosion or an ebbing of the tide. I suspect that soon after diagnosis, if I had asked Mum to describe her life at the stage of the disease she is at as I write these words, in mid-2004, when it has progressed to a moderate level, it may have been a different, grimmer picture than is her current subjective reality. I see in Mum a will to live, and to live how *she* wants to live, and in fact she is doing that as best she can. Of course if she could, she would choose not to have Alzheimer's disease, but she does have it. She also has a life full of family and friends and music and her garden and her own home, and mostly she enjoys that life. She will firmly tell anyone who asks now that she is content. She laughs, in fact, and says, 'I'm on bonus time – I've had my three-score years and ten! If I go tomorrow, that's fine.' Although during her bad patches she has questioned the point of going on living, there is rarely anything maudlin about her current state of mind.

What I've learned is that things unfold and you deal with

them as you go along. That's what I've seen Mum do. She focuses on the present and the immediately foreseeable future. Once she knew and absorbed the fact that she had Alzheimer's she contracted her vision substantially. I am sure this is partly the disease itself, and it is not unreasonable to suspect that in some way it also masks a certain amount of fear. But if you ask her about it, she laughs indignantly at you and accuses you of amateur psychology, of incorrectly second-guessing her. In her own conscious reality, life is quite okay, thank-you-very-much! That makes a certain kind of sense to me, and in fact I catch myself doing it in relation to her. It's foolish to not think ahead to some degree in terms of making practical arrangements but there are other ways in which there's just no advantage in trying to imagine which of a million variations the future might hold. In fact I was talking with her about it on the afternoon I was reviewing this chapter, and she reminded me of a saying she thought we should all stick on our walls or fridges: 'Why worry? It may not happen!' Some things can't be solved in advance, and the exact permutations of how the disease might affect Mum two years or five years from now is one of them.

I certainly found that I had to give myself plenty of time and take small steps when it came to my own early attempts to gather and absorb information about the disease. Like Mum, that's always something I have found useful, but in this case my heart wasn't in it. My desire to know could not overcome how painful I found the stories. I remember one book, for instance, that a kind friend lent me soon after Mum was diagnosed.

It was a compilation of carers and families talking about how they'd dealt with their loved ones' dementia, the progression of it and how they had handled it. I read about a third of it howling my eyes out but it was just too painful and I couldn't read the rest. I know that some people react very differently: they soak up the information, and find that having facts and details right there helps them enormously. But it was too raw, too bleak for me, and I found no comfort in those stories then. Instead it was almost like twisting the knife in the wound.

That has changed with the passage of time, so that now I want to listen to the stories of other people in a similar situation, and I can hear in them more of the positives amid the sadness and grief and trauma. I'm able to absorb the things that have worked, to appreciate the coping mechanisms or moments of joy or appreciation or courage or humour that are still there in the face of everything. But my own initial reaction of turning away made me realise how important it is to recognise that people are going to seek out information and support and help at their own pace. It can be offered, but it can't be forced. We are only ready to absorb whatever we can deal with at any particular point. And we need to have compassion for that. One way I could do that was by letting Mum be. If she wanted to talk about how she was feeling, that was fine with me, and if she preferred not to most of the time, that was fine too.

In her autobiography Mum described a habit she had at various turbulent times in her life of writing down her innermost thoughts – pouring out onto paper late at night the things she felt she couldn't say to anyone – and then burning the pages. She found relief in writing it all down. I don't know if she did that after the diagnosis. I never noticed any evidence of a paper journal that she kept or a temporary journal that she might destroy. For a time, a year or so in all, starting before her diagnosis, Prue and I tried hard to get her back to using her computer. We thought if we could get her writing on her computer again it would provide an easy way for her to progressively work on something – we could get it set up so she just turned it on and the last file she'd been working on would pop up. Then she could use it to write whatever she wanted, be it a journal or a shopping list. We tried first on the laptop on which she'd written her autobiography, and when she wasn't taking to that we traded it in and got her a desktop computer with a more comfortable keyboard and a bigger screen. We had somebody come in who teaches computer skills to people with diminished cognitive abilities – people who've been in car accidents and acquired brain injury, for instance. But the computer skills just weren't deeply embedded enough. We were a little bit late in terms of the progress of the disease, and Mum was a bit too defensive about it all. I was sad about that.

Some things worked, some didn't. Some things helped, some didn't. But in one way or another life rolled on, and we all coped as best we could. It wasn't too long before Mum started referring to her condition as 'The Big A'. I don't know if she invented this name for the disease, but I'd certainly never heard anyone use it before. I guess it's taken from 'The Big C', which is what you'd sometimes hear cancer called in the 1960s and '70s. It has a sort of power. It mocks the disease, and robs it of some of its fear and dread. It's a refusal to take it completely seriously. And yes, in a way it is whistling past the graveyard – putting on a show of not being afraid in the face of something that terrifies you. But I think there is power in that. It's a very Australian response, and a very Hazel response. It encapsulates her humour and her refusal to be cowed by this, or any other bloody thing!

But for all of her spirit and her courage, and the adaptations that were happening, we still had some pretty black times to get through.

# An Awful Anger

By the end of 2001, Mum had wound down all of her major work responsibilities. In November she had done some campaigning for the Federal election, but this time she could only manage to visit one electorate. Stepping back from public life wasn't driven by the diagnosis as such, more by a combination of the effects the early Alzheimer's was having on her – the difficulties it had brought in fulfilling those roles; the tiredness and tendency to withdraw – and a feeling that it was time to move on. She resigned as a board member of the Australian Children's Television Foundation, a role which had been dear to her heart. She had been a passionate supporter of quality Australian-made children's television programs for years, and a board member of the ACTF since 1984. Patricia Edgar and the other key staff and board members there were wonderfully supportive of Mum as it became clear that she needed more help towards the end of her time with them.

The members and staff of the NSW Heritage Council were similarly understanding. Mum had been chair since early 1997, although her deputy soon took over chairing the meetings at Mum's request, since this was a task in which she never felt particularly skilled or comfortable. She had focused from the beginning on community awareness: building participation, and an expanded sense of what it is to appreciate our heritage, in all its forms. She believed in the importance and value of the issues, and thoroughly enjoyed the time she spent working with the council. In the year or so before she resigned it was clear she needed more support to do this, but the council members and office staff had been very matter of fact about providing this.

Her commercial contracts, for Pioneer Homes and Herron Pharmaceuticals, also finished around this time, and again, both organisations had been very understanding in the final year or so when Mum's capacity was changing. Euan Murdoch, from Herron, was particularly encouraging and kind. (The fact that, with the help of these individuals and organisations, Mum was able to go on contributing in such a major way for so long, despite the challenges that came with her Alzheimer's, has some real lessons in it, I think.)

It was just as well, really, that she had already shed these roles, because just before Christmas 2001 Mum slipped on a rock while she was gardening and broke her left ankle. She was on her own at the time, and crawled all the way back up to the house, ran herself a bath, and rang our place. Jan answered, and heard the distress in her voice even before she said, 'I think I might've broken my leg.' He was round there in record time, and found her in the bath, into which she'd dropped the cordless phone. He called an ambulance and once again Mum was back in Royal North Shore Hospital.

The break itself wasn't particularly bad, but she needed to have some plates and screws put in her ankle, and this meant a general anaesthetic. Physically she wasn't too hard-hit – the operation was straightforward, and required only a few days in hospital; then she was back home with a cast on her ankle, and a wheelchair and crutches so she could move around. But mentally the change was striking. For whatever reason – the shock of the break itself, the disorientation of being admitted to hospital, the anaesthetic and surgery, or some combination of these factors – Mum was badly affected. She was way beyond forgetful. She didn't have a grasp of what was going on, and the smallest details threw her. We can all have temporary memory lapses or slight confusion, but they are momentary, and we're able to put the pieces back together and jog ourselves back into place. Mum's confusion was completely different. She just could not understand what was happening around her. It was distressing to see.

A similar dip in capacity had happened after her false-alarm 'heart attack', but this was much more pronounced. And while she didn't ever get quite back to the point she had been at before that first incident, she recovered substantially.

This time, in the months afterwards, she again recovered some of that lost capacity, but it took longer, and the recovery was not as strong as before. She was definitely changed, and not for the better.

Ros had moved up to Sydney from Canberra during the year, and stayed with Mum to help her while her ankle was mending. That worked well for a while but eventually it became clear that, apart from anything else, Mum was too fiercely possessive of her hard-won independence to want to live with anyone, even a beloved daughter doing her best to help, so we had to find another solution. This proved to be the beginning of a hellish period all round. In fact the 18 months that followed were probably the worst of my life.

During the months following the accident Mum got angrier and more frustrated and more negative than I had ever seen her. A lot of things fed those dark thoughts. I'm sure that partly it was the disease itself – the way it was affecting her brain at that time; partly it was her response to having to come to terms with the fact she had Alzheimer's; and partly it was a reaction to no longer being in control of her own life or domain, a situation she found intolerable. One manifestation of her emotional state was an uncharacteristic obsession with things she could do nothing about. She spent a lot of time going on and on about how bad some given thing or person was, or had been, and whipping herself up into tears and distress. Often I'd try to distract her, to lead her on to happier ground, but occasionally when that didn't work I'd find myself saying to her in frustration, 'Mum, what is the point in this conversation? I understand you feel upset but I don't want to keep talking over and over and over about it. You're just upsetting yourself and it's pissing me off.' Surprisingly, this sometimes worked to break the cycle and we were able to move on to more positive topics.

The other manifestation of her unhappiness was even harder to deal with. She was so angry, so much of the time. She was both aggressive and defensive and her behaviour was so out of character it shook us all badly.

What was going on with Mum would have been bad enough if it had been the only challenge my family faced, but inevitably it wasn't. I think this is one of the common truths about caring for someone with Alzheimer's that is so often overlooked: it's usually only one aspect of a wider family scenario, which is more than likely to include other challenges. It's not as if life's trickier bits always appear in easy-to-digest doses. In the latter part of 2002, as Mum got worse, our 13-year-old son, Ben, was going through a very tough time at school, which culminated in us having to move him to another one. Our daughter, Sophie, was doing her Higher School Certificate and like so many other teenagers, she was suffering from all the stress of that pressure-cooker final year of high school. Jan was also dealing with persistent unexplained agony that was eventually diagnosed as neuropathic pain – nerve damage resulting from a previous infection. The fact that Mum was so terribly unhappy, and so angry with the world, was upsetting in its own right, but the difficulty was exacerbated by all these other pressures on our little nuclear family.

Late 2002, early 2003, we had weeks of misery and rage from Mum. She was alternately suicidal and confrontational. She said she couldn't see the point in living and didn't want to go on anymore. She was furious. I had, of course, read about anger as one of the possible symptoms of Alzheimer's as the disease progresses, but I was still shocked by the reality of it. She had an awful, fiery anger that was completely atypical of her. There was some welcome respite when we went again to the annual January Buddhist retreat that we had previously attended together. But by the end of the retreat it was clear that she was deeply unhappy about some aspects of her life, and that those of us close to her had to do what we could to address this. On one particular day that I still remember with a shudder, she ended up pacing up and down in our backyard while talking loudly about all sorts of wild things she was going to do. Jan and I talked to her, trying alternately to reason, soothe and distract her, but any calm was short-lived and the distress would soon flare again. It was like trying to calm a raging bull. Finally I called Mum's doctor who came by and brought some Valium. It was the only way to alleviate her distress in the short term. It was a truly gruesome day.

During this turbulent period I kept reminding myself not to take it personally. I knew it was the disease, and her circumstances, driving it all. But I wasn't used to Mum being so angry at life, and when she was angry with me, that made it all the harder. Being the oldest child, I'd often been a sounding board, a confidante for her. During difficult times in her life she used to unburden herself to me, and that was a habit that went right back – she tells a story about me sitting on the step with her when I was two, comforting her while she had a cry after a fight with Dad.

So I have always had an awareness of the messier side of her life, and I've supported her through bad patches (as she has me), but this was unprecedented. And Mum knew it too, in her clearer moments. Often she would apologise. Indeed, after she came back to herself on the day of the backyard fury, she said to me, 'I'm sorry darling, I'm not really angry at you, I know you're doing what you can – it's these other things . . .' I knew that. I knew that it wasn't personal, and that this wasn't really what Mum was like, and I couldn't hold it against her. But I also knew that her being aware enough to apologise didn't mean it wouldn't happen again. And knowing all that didn't make seeing her like this, or enduring it, much easier.

This period culminated in what turned out to be a horror trip to Perth. A recurrent theme leading up to this had been her aggressive, yet inaccurate assertion of full independence. 'It's my life,' she'd say, 'if I fuck it up then bad luck – that's my problem and you lot can't babysit me. I haven't burnt the house down and I haven't left the gas on.' (In fact, Ros had found her once with the gas turned on and the flame out.) I had a lot of sympathy with her rage at her sense of powerlessness, and I was concerned that she not be 'over-supported'.

Although I accepted that she was entitled to assume her own risks, there was no doubt that she didn't fully realise some of those risks, nor that she needed more done for her than she perceived. She was determined to go to Perth to see my brother, Steve, and his family. And she was equally determined she would make the trip alone. This was plainly not a good idea. At the time she couldn't find her way from the front of my house to the back of it, and she wanted to get on a plane and go to the other side of the country on her own.

It was clear that she was in no condition to travel solo, so the only way she could get her wish to go was if someone flew with her. Jan rearranged the various demands on him so that they could go in February 2003, but her perception was so distorted that some of her energy in the lead-up to the trip was spent in fury at him. 'I don't need a fucking minder!', she shouted. The ugliness of the situation only got worse when they were on board the plane. They had before them a five-hour flight in a public environment so Jan tried tactfully to limit how much alcohol Mum had with her meal. But again, thanks to her distorted perceptions, she couldn't see any need for this – other than a malicious desire to control her – and she wasn't up to accurately monitoring her own consumption. She reached the point where she was telling him, 'I wanna go home' and starting to undo her seatbelt in order to get up and go to the flight deck so she could get the plane turned around. Jan did anything and everything he could to distract her, and somehow they made it to Perth without a major incident.

Jan saw Mum safely to the friend with whom she was staying, then went to my cousin's house and called me. He was really shaken. It was the 'flight from hell' and had left him drained and very upset. Neither of us knew whether Mum's anger and distress would pass or continue to grow, and if it did how we'd cope. As it happened, with one more flurry of drama in Perth, Mum would soon move into a much better frame of mind. But the stress of it all took a heavy toll. Jan became very ill again that year and I feel sure that his relapse was triggered by the strain he and the rest of the family were under.

In Perth, with loving friends, and away from the issues that had been distressing to her, Mum calmed down, but she was still convinced that her family was treating her like an idiot, taking over her life, putting unnecessary restraints on her and failing to recognise how capable she was. She told all this in no uncertain terms to her friends there. Despite the terrible shape she had been in just a few days before, she was able to paint a very plausible picture about her own capacity for independence and her interfering children who were refusing to allow her to live the way she wanted to.

Friends arranged, at her request, for her to see a GP in order to get a referral for a 'second opinion' on whether she had Alzheimer's disease. The Perth GP, her Sydney GP, Dr Richard Schloeffel, and my cousin Jim Baker, a Perth psychiatrist, were all eventually involved in getting Mum in to see Professor Osvaldo Almeida, an expert in geriatric psychiatry who happened to be based in Perth. From his report, I know she told Professor Almeida that she had been experiencing 'minor problems' with her memory. She also told him that she was managing her own cooking, shopping, medication and bill-paying without any difficulty, which had not actually been the case for some time. Given the circumstances, Professor Almeida was able to conduct much briefer tests than those Robyn Murray had given her, but even these showed memory impairment, cognitive difficulties and a decline in her ability to function rationally as a result. He concluded that she did, indeed, have mild Alzheimer's disease.

Mum was away for just a few weeks, but when she came back things were much more settled. What part her acceptance of the confirmation of her diagnosis played I don't know, but she wasn't nearly so hostile. She was living alone again, with daily visits from Ros (who was now living just 30 minutes' drive away) and me, and we started to talk with her about bringing in a carer from outside the family. She couldn't see the need for it, but at least when we talked about it she got stroppy rather than furious. Part of her refusal to accept that it was necessary was a result of the efforts we had all made so Mum felt she was still independent. For example, managing her own medication. That was the rod we had created for our own backs. Breaking that perception down so she could see she needed extra help, and it couldn't/shouldn't always be us who gave it to her, took a lot of work. And, given the effect of the disease, many repetitive conversations.

I remember one discussion when Jane Munro, a friend of Mum, and I were trying to get her to agree to somebody coming in two or three times a week to do some cooking and to sort out the medication. Mum thought she had the perfect answer to that: 'I get the newspaper so I know what day it is,' she declared. The conversation started going round and round, and this supposedly irrefutable argument kept coming up again and again. In fact, I started to count how many times she was saying it and then forgetting she had. When I got to 21 I'd just had it. I said, 'Mum, I can't do this anymore! You've told me that 21 times since I started counting. Twenty-two and I'm going to go bloody nuts!' Thankfully, we then got the giggles.

I know it is said that human beings, generally speaking, often resist change, that we cling to the familiar in the foolish assumption that we can somehow make concrete that which makes us feel secure. In the course of my personal studies at about this time I was reading some of the Buddhist teachings on impermanence, and the fact that a lot of our suffering arises from our discomfort with the fundamental reality that impermanence and change is, in fact, part of the very nature of existence. While in a deeper sense I find these teachings powerful, I must admit that at this stage I drew from them a more immediate comfort. 'This too shall pass' became a sort of mantra that helped me untangle myself from encroaching despair during some of the hairier moments.

I can laugh about it all now, but back then I sometimes

wanted to tear my bloody hair out. Or Mum's! She was so utterly convinced of her irrational beliefs. And I knew she was wrong. But there's something very, very powerful about a person for whom you have deep respect being convinced of their own delusions. It's like you're in a reality warp. How do you converse with someone in that state and maintain respect for their sense of self when the things they are saying are so off the mark?

As I've said, that bleak, black period was an absolute shocker. It had a major impact on all of us, the effects of which still linger. But even so, I consider us to be very fortunate. That was the worst of it. Which means all the rest, before and after, has been better. Generally speaking, Mum, in her character, her nature, is not a 'difficult' person at all – she is wonderful company, with a wise humour that tends to disarm, rather than exacerbate, conflict. We have an easier road than people whose loved ones remain more distressed or aggressive or disoriented. Ours was a horrible patch, and seemed a long one, but it was still only a patch, thank god!

CHAPTER 8

# The Choices We Make

FROM TIME TO TIME, people have said that they don't think what's happened to Mum is 'fair'. In one of the emails we got after *Australian Story* aired, someone wrote that she was 'the last person in the world to deserve this fate'. I can understand this reaction – too well! – and have a sense of the kinds of things people mean when they say it: perhaps that they would have liked her to have had more time to enjoy the life she built after the marriage split; that it's sad that she didn't get a clear shot at doing all the things she might have liked to do before the fog of Alzheimer's started creeping in; or just that she seems such a good, decent person that there is no sense of justice in this fate befalling her. I too wish she didn't have the disease, but I can't sustain thinking of it in these terms.

It seems to me that regarding things as unfair or unjust, in the context of a (currently) non-preventable disease, or any other 'random' fate, doesn't do any good at all, for anyone. It can lead to a useless sort of resentment or bitterness – and against what? To entertain any notion of 'justice' seems to imply that maybe there are some people who do 'deserve' it. And how could you wish this disease upon anyone at all, really? It's a simple, unpalatable truth that 'bad' things happen to 'good' people. To wonder why is to enter a realm of speculation about the nature of the universe that is beyond me, or the scope of this story. As I once heard somebody say, 'Try telling the stars you're angry.' It doesn't change anything.

One of my favourite prayers is the serenity prayer: 'Give me the serenity to accept the things I cannot change, courage to change those I can, and wisdom to know the difference.' I can't change the fact that my mother has Alzheimer's. Nobody's done it to her. Nobody has caused her to have it. And nobody can change the fact that she does have it. There are plenty of evils in the world that maybe, with sufficient will, we could change – the fact that 18,000 children under five die of hunger every day comes to mind. It seems to me that these are the things worth being angry about, if that can spur us to doing something about them.

But I don't rail against fate for my mother's disease. To me it's not unjust or unfair. It's unfortunate, it's regrettable, and it's something that sometimes makes me terribly sad. However, if a sense of the impact of Alzheimer's is brought home to us through our knowledge of Mum having it, then she herself also models the most constructive direction our response can take. And that is to realise how very many people are dealing with it now, and will face it in years to come. And to examine our attitudes and support for those people in the present, and to contribute towards the possibility that it may cause less suffering for others in future.

Mum's own way of dealing with it is mostly about accepting how things are. It's not that she is never angry or frustrated about it, but self-pity doesn't get a look-in. I've never heard her lament 'Why me?' In recent months her mood during the day, and most nights, has been cheerful and matter of fact. I've noticed that the anger only becomes predominant if she has been drinking alcohol. She has a funny habit of 'talking to God', calling him Huey, and she'll sometimes point upwards and talk about the things that Huey should fix. She's somewhat ambivalent about whether 'He' even exists, but nevertheless she'll occasionally tell him that he's given her a bum deal with her having Alzheimer's, and the same for anybody else who has it. But it's usually done with humour. She's not ranting or whingeing to 'an unfair God', she's simply registering her views on the way she'd like the world to be. And characteristically she does it by refusing to take things too seriously. In fact, some of our funnier moments are when we have a cup of tea together – me, Mum, and Huey.

Another subject people sometimes broach is what you might call the built-in death sentence that comes with Alzheimer's. The general medical expectation seems to be that the person will have eight to 10 years from the onset of obvious symptoms to death. And often it is not the disease itself that kills them. It might well be one of the other causes of death, such as a heart attack or pneumonia, that older people often succumb to. (After all, 50 per cent of Australians with dementia are over 85.) But if nothing else gets you, the Alzheimer's will. Eventually it will have closed down so much of the brain that the bodily functions it regulates start to fail. This is not a disease, like, for example, breast cancer, where doctors talk about the survival rate. Nevertheless, we obviously don't know how the future will specifically unfold. Mum could be hit by a bus tomorrow – as could any of us. Heaven forbid, as the saying goes, but we just don't know. And because we don't know and couldn't necessarily change it if we did, I suppose I believe that these thoughts are rather pointless. It doesn't mean I don't have them. But they are less frequent, paradoxically, as time passes, and their grip has lessened as I've learned to count our blessings in the present.

Don't get me wrong, I'm not saying that the 'sentence' associated with Alzheimer's doesn't cast a shadow. It does. But life is dominated by shadows if we spend too much energy preoccupied with the sad, the bad, and the what-could-be's. It can crowd out any room for awareness or appreciation of whatever is good around us. I believe that we have an element of choice about what we will worry about and what we won't, and I suspect the seeds of this belief were very much sown by the way Mum herself – indeed both my parents – tend to approach life.

If I am honest with myself then my ultimate answer to the 'built-in sentence' is, well you wouldn't want it to be longer, would you? I'm not saying I want Mum to die. But, of course, she will. And given the nature of the disease, what I wish for her is that when the time comes that her quality and enjoyment of life is too diminished, she goes easily and peacefully and painlessly, and doesn't experience too much further suffering from the disease, or from anything else. I also try to bring openness to the way I think about what might happen if Mum survives long enough to develop end-stage dementia and seems to be beyond any real communication or awareness. I know that when my mind goes there it's really uncomfortable. I hate the thought of her being like that. I just try to tentatively walk through those thoughts and think about it bit by bit. That way I give myself the best chance of not sinking into a hole about it.

The place my mind goes first is, what is that going to be like for her? It may freak me out, and represent the fate Mum least wanted for her final years, but will it actually be horrible for *her* if it happens? Will *her* experience of her life at that time be unhappy? Thinking little by little about it helps me to realise that while I now feel that seeing Mum so profoundly damaged would horrify me, I can also anticipate that if she were not distressed there could be a kind of acceptance on my part. Reading much of the correspondence we have received, and talking to others who have lived through their loved ones dying with this disease, reinforces my sense of this possibility of acceptance. I remember Mum's GP, Dr Schloeffel, saying to me early on that, in his experience, there comes a point where the family suffers more than the person with the disease. That the person's awareness diminishes to a point where the suffering often reduces, and greater contentment sets in.

Certainly I wonder deeply about Mum's experience of her life now, and how it will be in future. Of course we talk, during the spectrum of ongoing conversations, about her moods or thoughts, as about many other things. But despite her firm assertion that she really, overall, is fine, I can't help but wonder about her deep internal reality. It's as if our conversations are more confined to a narrowing tip of the iceberg of experience than they used to be – not deliberately, or by any diminished sense of closeness, but by the impacts of the disease. And I wonder about the rest of the iceberg. As the disease gradually progresses, so does the capacity to articulate experience, so that experience becomes, in a way, less accessible to us left on the 'outside'. There have been numerous documented cases of coma patients who seem to be beyond reach, but who come back to consciousness and describe things that happened in the hospital room around them while they were comatose. Enough to make, you wonder about what is being perceived and experienced beneath the level of conscious recognition.

It seems absurd, and somehow disrespectful, to assume because it is becoming less accessible to us, and in some ways to them, that the internal world of people with dementia is 'less'. But dementia sufferers have 'no road out'. They don't 'come to' and tell us what was happening for them. So one of the big imponderables for me is what Mum's internal experience really is. And how is that changing as the disease progresses? For instance, what is her experience of those occasions when to all outward perception she loses track of time and sits doing nothing, hardly moving, for a stretch of time. Is that long and boring to her, or as her sense of time disappears does her sense of tedium disappear too? And does her apparently diminishing awareness of her condition also diminish her fear of the future?

Given that I'll never know the answers to those questions, the touchstone I use in everything to do with her Alzheimer's is: how happy is Mum? If she is in a good patch and her mood seems to be good, if she is cheerful and reasonably content from moment to moment, then I think that's the best guide we have. In a way, that sounds obvious. But it's all too easy to fall into a trap of thinking things *should* be this way, or *ought* to be that way; that your responsibility is to provide 'perfect care'and that if you don't you are letting down the person you love. Whereas I think it's often easier and more effective to let the person you're caring for guide you by their happiness, or lack of it.

It's much easier for me to be calm and philosophical now than it was during that horror stretch. But even though I've been well conditioned to see the positive by my parents, there are times when that ability has deserted me. I would hate to give the impression that I always cope well. I don't.

When I was enmeshed in the confluence of all those dramas and traumas, with Mum, Jan, Sophie and Ben all having their own major difficulties, I felt like there was nothing much else. I felt responsible for so many things on so many fronts that I became unwell and overanxious myself and ended up on anti-depressant medication. That feeling, of drowning in competing demands and dramas, is very common to carers, because you can't pull the strand of Alzheimer's out of the rest of your life. It doesn't work like that. Much as we may wish we could compartmentalise or quarantine the various dramas away from some 'normal' life, they seem to take on, for a time, an overwhelming quality that can *become* the tone of your life. In fact, friends I could rely on for their black humour told me I should write a script – their kindly queries of 'How are you?' would be met with a running update that seemed like another instalment in a B-grade soap. There were days when I would ham it up for myself or friends – if you feel stuck in the middle of a woeful movie you might as well appreciate the absurdity of it all.

One of the big stresses of being a carer for someone with Alzheimer's is that you're dealing with this thing that is preoccupying you and taking up an increasing amount of internal space and time and resources that are needed in other areas of your life. It's most often women who find themselves in this unsustainable situation. In fact there's a term for it now: the sandwich generation. As we tend towards having kids older, more of us will find ourselves with relatively young children with all their needs on one side, and elderly parents, who may have dementia or other serious conditions, on the other. (As well as dealing with such mundane necessities as earning a living!) Both sides require time and energy – it's no wonder that the pressure in the middle can seem intense at times.

Everyone has their own way of coping in those situations. If I'm asked what works best for me I feel rather at a loss, as I have no 'formula'. When things seem bad, I suppose the number one remedy is time out, however brief, and using this to turn my attention away from the thoughts that are disturbing me towards something pleasant and nurturing. Often music, meditation, a break in the sun staring aimlessly at nature, a laugh with a friend, or a walk on the beach will do the trick. And a warm bath with lavender oil in it can work wonders. But if I'm particularly perturbed I find television is wonderful therapy! It works terrifically well because 'packaged' distraction from pain is sometimes the most constructive thing you can do. And although reading has always been tremendously important to me, there were times in the past couple of years when I just could not read much. I didn't have what it took to focus on the book; my own circular thoughts would keep intruding. But I could sit and watch television. Junk television was really good and I watched a lot of it, with no apologies. At times of greatest stress I could have recited parts of the TV schedule. Occasionally I would tell myself off for wasting the small parts of my life that were left over after all the dramas, but I knew it was just a way of getting through the patches when my own resources were almost empty and I needed 'blank' time.

Of course this sort of strategy, while bringing a welcome 'numbness' at the time, doesn't really do much to support a deeper resilience or sense of wellbeing. My longer term, more productive way of coping is to try to keep fit and well, in the broadest sense. Exercise makes a clear difference – walking and yoga are the types that work best for me. Making sure I see friends, or at least talk to them on the phone, is another big one. Then there's my sense of humour, which can be very black – it's something that runs strongly in my family. With trusted friends I can find humour in just about anything, knowing that they will neither misinterpret nor repeat our conversations. Even when I'm feeling at my worst I can usually see something horribly funny if I'm talking to a friend with a similarly warped sense of humour. That got me through some of the most intense stress periods of 2002 and 2003: being able to crack awful jokes about my mother and my husband and my son and all the people who were having dramas around me. My friends knew me well enough to know that saying dreadful things about a person or situation is just using black humour as a way of coping, and it can really let some of the pressure out.

My Buddhist study and meditation practice is something else I find invaluable. My ideal is to have a daily meditation session, even if it's just a few minutes; to read or listen to some of the great teachers; to study or practise occasionally with friends; and to attend occasional retreats. These things sometimes slide in times of sustained stress, but it's worth the effort to fit them in, since I have found, repeatedly, that they make such a difference.

This issue of how carers care for themselves is one that is so important, but can be so easily ignored, with serious consequences (and, of course, this doesn't just apply to caring for someone with Alzheimer's). The more care is needed, the more it becomes an issue.

It's too easy to have Alzheimer's *be* the context, to let it dominate your sense of the person with it, and of your relationship with them. But that's something all carers have to fight against, both out of respect for the person with the disease, and because while there will be times when it does dominate, it's when that doesn't stop, when it seems that the Alzheimer's is all there is, that you can go under. The times I've felt like I was drowning have been when it seemed all there was around me was people's problems and trauma. Just like so many carers before me, I've found that the key to surviving is to create a context for yourself that allows for more than just that. It can be a similar process to something many of us went through when our children were young: if you don't find ways to make sure that the thread of your life beyond your role as a mother is still strong (however deeply valued that role is), then things can become limited for everyone – for your children, your partner and for yourself.

With Alzheimer's there are some particular symptoms and general requirements of care that can stretch every nerve when you're already stressed. There is a very popular book that Alzheimer's Australia (AA) sells whose title sums up what it can be like: *The 36-Hour Day*. I cannot pretend to know what this is like over an extended period of time – Mum is still too competent and independent in much of her day-to-day life for this to be the case for me. But there have been patches that have given me a sense of how it could be. When times have been bad, caring for Mum has seemed to be detail after relentless bloody repetitive detail. And the repetitive questioning can be hard to cope with – that's something that gets to almost all carers sooner or later.

Carers who don't have anything set up that allows them to get out of that role for a break and who don't have any other support around them can even find themselves snapping. Lewis Kaplan from AA has talked about carers who come to the AA counselling service in a terrible state because they've reached breaking point in an awful swirl of exhaustion and stress and frustration, and they've hit the person they're caring for. I have never hit Mum but I have yelled at her, and have felt awful afterwards – lower than low.

You figure out how to be a 'carer' as you go along, just as you do with raising kids and so many other crucial things in life. There's no education that prepares you ahead of time. Along the way I have found that I need to have different coping strategies for different stresses. One of them is what to do under immediate duress. When my children were young I found that 'time out' was a very useful device when the situation was getting overheated: five minutes out of the room could often defuse developing frustration or conflict. (Although the classic 'time-out' involves the kids going to their room, I often found it simpler to remove myself for a few minutes!) So if I find myself feeling exasperated I'll often just take myself out of the conversation for 30 seconds, or take myself out of the room for a few minutes. A few moments' solitude in my bedroom or in the garden can work wonders. I know that sometimes it's easy to get caught up, to not think of stepping away for even a few moments. Or to think that if you do, things may worsen. But my observation is that's hardly ever the case. If you do leave the room for a few minutes you might come back to a big (or bigger) mess, but then again things might have calmed down, the heat might have gone out of the situation, the other person may be distracted from whatever seemed to be the problem. Yes, your choices are going to have consequences but you don't always know what those consequences are going to be, even when you may think you do.

In fact, a sense of choice itself is something that I have realised is really important to me in terms of Mum's Alzheimer's, as in any situation. I feel, from experience, that an authentic sense of choice generates more optimism, and power to positively affect a situation, than feeling like a victim does. I don't see this as merely a philosophical question – it's also a matter of operational self-interest. It's crucial for my own feeling of wellbeing that I don't fall into the trap of thinking,

'Well I *have* to care for Mum . . .' Because I don't. I don't *have* to, I choose to. I think it empowers me and sustains me to recognise that. The other option I have in this situation, the option of not being involved in Mum's care, is one I reject. But recognising that it is an option, even if it's one that's unacceptable to me, reminds me sometimes of what's important.

I have also come to realise that worry is a choice, too. I could spend my waking hours worrying myself silly about all sorts of things: what Mum is eating and how I can make sure her clothes are spotless every time she steps out her front door, whether she is safe to walk to the local shops and back each day, and about the lonely patches I know she has at times. But if I did I'd be less use to her or myself or anyone else, unable to address the issues calmly and see what, pragmatically, can be done. And she would have less sense of independence or self-determination.

Instead, I have developed a sort of 'Is it good enough?' test. I don't mean: is it good enough so we can get away with it? It's not about being slapdash or not caring. But: is Mum's nutrition really good enough? And the answer is 'yes'. Is it optimal? No. She lives alone, at her insistence, and no longer cooks much. She has meals provided by me sometimes and she has food prepared and ready for her to put together without cooking on some other days. Her carer, Gail, helps with her shopping, making sure there are always things in the fridge to snack at. Doubtless if she were still cooking the wonderful food she did for many years she would be eating even better than she is. But her nutrition is sound enough.

The same with her grooming. Is it perfect? No. Is it good enough when it matters? Yes. I have let go of the notion that I can guard the way Mum looks when she goes on her daily walk to the local shops. That's her local place, it's her village. People are accepting and protective of her. If she has a coffee spill on her top, so be it. But if she's going out into a more public arena I'll make sure that she looks just the way she would want to in that context.

I realise that you could take the 'Is it good enough?' test as a cop-out. But I don't think that's so. I believe that to care enough is to support self-respect, to support a subjective perception of independence, to support contentment, and to balance this against the ideal of everything you could possibly put in place. Fussing constantly might get some aspects of Mum's life one or two notches closer to some arbitrary measure of supposed perfection, but the cost for her and for me would be high. Another thing I have come to see as crucial to surviving difficulty is compassion, towards other people and towards yourself. Compassion is not some woolly word or something to talk about in church on Sundays. I think it's one of the basic qualities of being human and it's one we can nurture and cultivate in ourselves and in others. It doesn't matter what your belief system is, compassion works.

As a carer you have to bring compassion to yourself. If you are caring for someone with Alzheimer's, there is so much potential guilt and anxiety about every aspect of their lives and the progress of the disease that you are inevitably critical of yourself at times. You want things to be as 'perfect' as possible. But in most cases, if it was a friend who was in the same situation you'd say to them, 'For heaven's sake, you're doing your best. You're crazy to judge yourself so harshly. Look at everything you're juggling. You're actually doing a great job.' And in a way you have to talk to yourself like you would talk to a loved friend. You need to do that because maybe everybody else around you is too distracted or busy to say it to you, or they don't actually know you're undermining yourself with neurotic fears or self-judgement. So first and foremost you have to bring that sort of compassion to yourself, and then you'll be more able to extend it to the people around you. I don't think of this as either noble or self-serving but rather as a necessary ingredient of living happily with yourself and others.

At the height of that terrible period I've described earlier, I realised I needed help to cope, and sought advice from Robyn Murray, who is a counsellor as well as neuropsychologist. Talking things through with her, and with another counsellor, was very useful. And I made sure I sought advice and support before making significant decisions. I also saw a doctor who prescribed anti-depressant medication after commenting that I wasn't depressed, but was 'understandably rather anxious'. The medication helped me through the toughest times, but it is coming to realisations like the ones above that empower choice and compassion and are therefore of lasting value. And so is the recognition that while it's no good to try to suppress the sadness I have about Mum having Alzheimer's, there is no good either in magnifying it, or in missing the many wonderful moments along the way. We're in this for the long haul, and the learning and insights offered by the journey itself are crucial to making the best of it.

CHAPTER 9

# Deciding to Go Public

THE SEARCH FOR THE right person to come in and help with Mum's meds, food and other tasks took a while. It didn't seem necessary for them to have had experience specifically with dementia, but we needed to feel sure they could understand the practical implications of it quickly. What was most important was that they saw Mum as a person, and not as a disease or condition. They needed to be trustworthy and discreet – this was before Mum made her Alzheimer's public. And given Mum's resistance to the idea, they needed to be flexible and wise enough to deal with her without aggravating the situation; to go with her flow rather than imposing a routine.

The vehemence with which Mum objected to the whole process waxed and waned but it never disappeared. I understood why. This was the most explicit action we'd taken against her wishes. She was saying she was competent to do what she needed without this help and we were saying, 'No, you're not.' Of course it hurt her. Of course she reacted badly to it.

We had reached, reluctantly, the point where we knew that many of Mum's perceptions were not to be relied on. For instance, with her medications we knew we had to take charge despite Mum's views to the contrary. But with that and with everything else so far it hadn't needed to be a big confrontation. We could rely on the fact that we could do things for her in a way that allowed her to think she was still doing certain tasks herself. We didn't have to argue it out or confront her with the view that her sense of herself was no longer fully accurate. This was different. We couldn't just throw a carer into the situation and hope Mum wouldn't notice! The process was painful for everyone.

But we couldn't put it off any longer. It wasn't that Mum needed so much care at that point that Ros and I couldn't take care of it between us. For the time being we could, although it was certainly awkward occasionally, given the other demands in our lives. However the number of things with which Mum needed help was growing, and we knew that was only going to continue. In terms of her food, we thought it would be good to have someone leave prepared meals for her, and ingredients that she could put together herself easily. There was also a safety issue in that Mum had lost her sense of smell when she had the pituitary operation. That was unconnected to the Alzheimer's but the combination of no sense of smell and her increasing lack of clarity about time meant she couldn't tell if milk or other food had gone off in her fridge.

Her shopping had become quite erratic, too. We would find all sorts of lists around the house, and there was no guarantee that the one she took with her was current. Either Ros or I usually took Mum to the local supermarket and did our shopping alongside her. I would sometimes slip things into her trolley that I knew she needed, or remove things that seemed a bit odd or unnecessary for her. But I'd have to be sneaky about it because otherwise she'd get very stroppy about my 'interfering'.

We also wanted to make sure that at least once a day someone checked in with her to make sure she was okay. Ros and I needed to know that if for some reason neither of us could do it then there would be a back-up with whom she was familiar. Just to see her and talk to her to find out how she was, and to make some direct observation to get around the problem of Mum's jumbled perceptions. For instance, at one point she was regularly telling me that her leg was sore and she'd show me where on the leg. But I realised that sometimes she was indicating the right and sometimes it was the left, sometimes the knee and sometimes the ankle. Seeing her daily, and not just talking to her on the phone, was the best way to get around the increasing 'false reports'. Then we could figure out what was really a problem and take care of it.

I'd started to feel that as the level of care Mum needed increased, and we struggled with the issues of implementing it, it was important to have someone outside the family provide some of that care. I wanted to make sure that we still had a relationship with Mum that was about family, rather than everything being subsumed into the 'carer' role. We could be more her daughters, son-in-law, grandchildren, if we weren't constantly having to act as nurses or minders (or 'bossy boots' – said sometimes with affection, sometimes not!).

So, family and close friends were convinced that Mum did need someone else in the mix, and we wanted to get her to the point where she would agree. We wanted that 'permission' for our own comfort, sure. But we also thought it was important in terms of minimising the ongoing stress for Mum. This person was to be going into her house several times a week, and if Mum was hostile and aggravated it would be upsetting for her and difficult for the carer to do what needed to be done. The more we could create acceptance for the idea by Mum the smoother it would be emotionally and practically.

We thought we might be on to a winner with the idea of comparing the help she'd be getting from a carer to the help that surrounded her in the Lodge years: 'You had people around you all the time then, doing all these things for you. You didn't take it as an insult then. You weren't upset about it then. What's the problem now?' But she wasn't buying that for a minute. She knew that there was a completely different set of reasons for it this time round. And, she said, 'This is my house, not the Lodge.'

In the end we weren't able to really convince her to get some home help (although a letter from Dr Schloeffel, saying he felt it was necessary and would help her to maintain her independence as much as possible, helped a bit).

We had to just go ahead. I couldn't help but laugh when we brought the first candidate around to meet her. Mum sat there, pinned this woman's gaze and said, 'I don't agree with this. I don't think it's necessary. I don't really know why you're coming and I don't want you to come.' She paused and made a stab at graciousness by adding, 'but I promise I'll behave decently'.

So we had to go ahead without winning Mum over, and we did, settling on a lovely woman called Susie. Sometimes Mum would be okay with Susie and sometimes she wouldn't. There were great days, and then occasionally Susie would have to put up with some quite tetchy behaviour. On the days when Mum was really making plain her negative feelings about the idea of a carer, Susie would go in and do the minimum and then leave as soon as she could, so as to cause the least upset. And once or twice she called me to say that given the reception when she'd turned up she'd decided it wasn't a smart idea to try to stay. Those days I'd pop round later to give Mum her meds and check in with her.

Over about four months Mum's hostility eased, she grew to grudgingly accept the idea of somebody coming in, and established more of a relationship with Susie. Then Susie left because she was moving out of Sydney, and we had to go through the search again. This time Ros and family friend Jane Munro did the work and settled on the wonderful Gail, who started about mid-2003 and still works for Mum for a couple of hours a few days a week. Like Susie, Gail has a great ability to judge the situation and respond to whatever's happening that day. Mum totally accepts her now and she has become part of Mum's landscape, with a routine of tasks on different days of the week.

It wasn't only on this issue that Mum grew more accepting as the year went on. Her general anger and hostility decreased too. From the lowest point at the start of 2003 she gradually became more relaxed and at peace with her life. Her sense of humour, which had been largely missing in action, returned. It's always been one of her more prominent traits, but for a while there it evaporated. You could see why, given the horror of what was happening to her, but it was good to see it back.

I think there were a few elements contributing to the improvement in her emotional state that happened over the latter part of the year. Her life became more settled: she was living alone again, which is what she wants; Gail was coming regularly; and after the Perth visit Mum made no other major trips for a while. There was less change, and change is demanding for people with cognitive problems. Stability is comforting. Even more important, I suspect, was the greater level of internal acceptance that I think Mum was reaching. She seldom talked directly about it, but from the odd reference, and her more settled demeanour, I felt strongly that she was coming more to terms within herself with what was happening to her. It was not a happy acceptance, but a form of acceptance nevertheless. The initial horror started to diminish and she started to feel more at ease with herself.

I think her acceptance was aided by the changes to her brain function that were happening during this period. Mum was no longer so aware of the fact that she wasn't functioning as well as she used to. As her cognitive capacity declined, so did her perception of that diminished capacity. In the early stages of Alzheimer's, Mum's awareness provoked constant frustration and confrontation. But as the disease has progressed that awareness has diminished and so have its emotional consequences.

As THE EFFECTS OF the Alzheimer's became more marked I was faced with the question of how to deal with making the news public. We knew it was going to come out eventually but we wanted to determine how and when and how much control we would have over the process. The rumours were already out there. In the year or two previously there had been whisperings, in political and other circles. Some of these had included speculation about some form of dementia, others had included the word Alzheimer's specifically. I'd had a lot of experience in ignoring political rumours and hosing down speculation, so that's what I did.

We also started to get media approaches: newspapers and magazines in particular calling to see 'how Hazel is'. Given that I was running Mum's office, and had managed her contact with the media since her separation from Dad, it was natural for me to deal with them. Usually nothing was said explicitly about Alzheimer's but I got the strong sense that they'd heard the rumours and wanted to check out exactly what was going on with her. Then a couple of media approaches came through that were more explicit, and I had to pull out every stop in order to kill these off without telling outright lies. I spoke off the record, as I always did on this subject, and said something like, 'I can neither confirm nor deny that because the only absolute confirmation of Alzheimer's is by autopsy and we haven't reached that point yet, so . . .' That worked; they backed off. What I said was the truth and that was part of it, but I think by putting it so bluntly, so pointedly, it was calling their bluff in a way. Fortunately no-one tried the direct tactic of saying 'We've heard a rumour that Hazel has Alzheimer's and we're printing it as a rumour. Would you care to make a comment?'

We were able to keep the story quiet for a long time partly because there is so much goodwill towards Mum and that runs through the people who work in media as well as the wider community. To go ahead and print a rumour after I'd made the autopsy comment would have been, in a sense, out of character with that goodwill. It was a gamble, though, and I was very relieved that it worked.

Then we had another close call and this time I tacitly acknowledged that yes, Mum was ageing and age was bringing changes with it, but I asked them out of respect not to go into it in print. Fortunately they agreed, but it was clear that I wouldn't be able to keep killing off stories for very much longer. I wondered occasionally if it was silly to even be concerned about public disclosure – it was nothing to be ashamed of, and it was hard to believe, in a way, that anyone would be particularly interested. But two things fed my sense that the possibility of the news becoming public should be taken seriously. One was the persistent enquiry from media, and the second was Mum's own sensitivity to feeling diminished by how people would see it.

At this point people who didn't know Mum well could still have a casual conversation with her and if they didn't know any different factually, if they just took what she said at face value and had no experience with dementia, they would see that her memory was slipping but might not figure out anything much else was wrong. This did lead to some awkward situations, some that are funny looking back, but weren't so funny at the time. One night during this period I had a call from Ros, who'd been trying to phone Mum but she wasn't answering. It was about 10.00 pm and she'd been trying for hours with no luck. We both knew that sometimes Mum didn't put the phone back on the hook properly, and if we popped around to check, she was fine. But this was not an engaged signal, the phone was ringing out. It was a long time since

Mum had independently made any spontaneous social arrangements, and I knew she didn't have any concerts or other outings arranged for that night. It had been a wet and windy afternoon, so Mum was unlikely to have been out walking, leading to a neighbourhood drop-in. I agreed with Ros that it was potentially concerning. But I'd been working hard and was having trouble sleeping. I knew I had a busy day ahead, so I'd just taken a sleeping pill. That meant that I didn't want to do what I normally would in this situation, and jump in the car and call around to Mum's.

Instead I rang one of Mum's neighbours, John, and asked if he could go to her house, see if there were any lights on and knock on the door. Mum usually leaves a light or two on if she goes out, but there were no lights on. Kind man that he is, he tried shining a torch in through the window in case she'd fallen and hurt herself before dark. He called me back about 10 minutes later saying, 'I can't raise her. She's probably asleep but I couldn't see.' Now I really was concerned, so I fought off the effects of the pill as best I could and got myself around there, with a key. By now it was raining hard. John met me outside and we let ourselves in – me fearing what we might find – but no Mum. It was late at night, pouring, Mum had no appointments and she wasn't at home. This was not looking good. Armed with torches and raincoats, John and I then searched her garden, and the bush down the back where she'd previously broken her ankle, but there was still no sign of her.

I was racking my brain to think where on earth she might be, or who might have seen her at any point that evening. Late as it was, I went back to John's house and rang around some of the other neighbours whose places she might have called in at. She wasn't at any of them, although one of the neighbours I called was a lovely woman called Janice whose daughter answered and said, 'Oh no, Mum and your Mum are going out tomorrow night but she's not here tonight.' I wasn't left with much to go on, and was reluctant to escalate the drama, but knew I needed to locate Mum somehow. I was stumped, but then an idea struck me. I know, I thought, I'll go into Mum's and hit redial on her phone. That'll tell me who she last spoke to and I can see if she made or mentioned some arrangement she didn't tell me about. (I think I may have been watching too many TV detective shows around that time!)

John and I were near Mum's driveway when a car we didn't recognise pulled in. It had barely stopped when the two of us loomed out of the darkness, dripping wet and shining our torches in at the occupants, who turned out to be Mum and Janice. They did indeed have an outing planned for the following night but had run into each other that afternoon and started chatting and Janice had asked Mum if she was interested in going along to a meeting she was attending about local bush regeneration. Because Mum hadn't 'gone public' I felt I couldn't explain to Janice, there and then, why I'd been so worried. And because Mum was still quite 'normal' in casual conversation, Janice probably couldn't figure out what I was doing acting like the anxious parent of a teenager who had stayed out late without permission. As nice as she was, she didn't say anything, although I felt I could see her thinking, 'What is this poor woman doing with this neurotic daughter interfering in her life?'

But the disease was progressing and it wasn't going to be too much longer before it would be clear to everyone that Mum had something more than a bit of memory loss going on. And there was always the possibility that she might be involved in an episode that turned into a 'newsworthy' incident. What if she was out, for instance, and something unexpected happened and she became confused and disoriented, clearly just didn't know what was going on? A journalist wouldn't even have to be there. All it would take would be for someone to call a newspaper and the story would be public. (I know it seems paranoid, but I had learned from experience that such things happen.) If something like that did happen, then all the goodwill in the world wouldn't be able to get the cat back in the bag.

I respected the people in the media and knew that covering something like that would be their job. I could also predict how it would unfold if the story did get out that way – one outlet would break the story and then we'd likely be deluged with others seeking comment and follow-up interviews. And however sympathetic they might be, I didn't want Mum to have to deal with that, and couldn't see any good coming from it. Running around trying to do damage control was a very unappealing prospect. That it was going to come out was increasingly inevitable, so I started to think more specifically about how we could (a) minimise harm or embarrassment to Mum, (b) maximise a sense of accomplishment for her, and (c) maximise the positive social impact of it. We knew we had to deal with it, and we knew we wanted to be in control. And given Mum's life-work of speaking out to help others, we knew we wanted that to be a focus.

We had talked about all this earlier, at the time of diagnosis, and Mum had basically said that while she thought, in principle, she might do something about telling the media one day, she was definitely not up for it so soon after hearing the news herself. She could see the sense in controlling the way she 'came out', but she wasn't quite ready. We'd discuss it and she'd say, 'Yes . . . but . . .' She just wasn't prepared to take that irrevocable step. She was understandably worried about the stigma and the sense of powerlessness that went with it.

She had always been a powerful advocate of tolerance and compassion, she'd always stood up and argued for that for other people. But no matter how much you believe in the issues, when you're the one feeling the pain and uncertainty of your own changing perceptions of yourself it's a big ask to find the courage to step into that spotlight. So I understood when Mum said she wanted more time. We let it lie for a while, but I kept her informed of the developments in media interest and we had an understanding that the issue was under loose ongoing review.

Mid-year in 2003 we seriously considered an approach from a magazine with which we'd long had a good relationship. Mum gave a lot of thought to agreeing to their request to do a major feature on her, but in the end she felt she still wasn't ready. And as much as I thought the time was approaching when we would need to make our own running on this, if Mum said doing the story didn't sit right for her, that overrode any of my concerns. She was entitled to say no. It was her life.

A couple of months passed and we had a tentative but, as it turned out, very fortuitous approach from the NSW branch of Alzheimer's Australia. One of AA's board members, Barbara Cail, had heard some of the rumours about Mum and that had started her thinking about the possibility of Mum taking on some kind of public role to promote the organisation and its work. Barbara is an old friend of Wendy McCarthy, and she knew that Wendy was close to Mum. So Barbara called Wendy to ask if she thought Mum might be interested and willing. Wendy then had a 'temperature-taking' conversation with Mum and got a favourable response, in principle. Wendy then called me, told me about Barbara's approach and about her exploratory conversation with Mum. As a result, she thought it was worth considering. I did, too, so Wendy, Barbara, AA NSW chief executive Lewis Kaplan and I met.

Mum didn't come to that meeting because I wanted to make

sure that anything we were exploring with people we didn't know was going to be sussed out first by me and Wendy. If we felt right about the way the conversation went we'd then take it to Mum. The meeting went well. We did some brainstorming, including the possibility that Mum would become a patron of Alzheimer's Australia, and then say something publicly about having it herself. I spoke about my strong feelings that we should, in Mum's interest, control the way the information went out, and attempt to reflect the way Mum would want it done, and what she would hope it might achieve. We talked about different ways we might do that in a speculative attempt to work out the best way forward, then someone suggested *Australian Story*. I liked the show and knew it was very well respected. Wendy knew it well and admired it a great deal, and spoke highly of the work of producer Helen Grasswill in particular.

We left the meeting with a loose plan: Wendy and I would have a series of conversations, separately and together, with Mum, to explore whether she would really be willing to do this. And because of the delicacy of the situation – we didn't want Mum to keep having to think about something like this if it wasn't going to happen – Wendy would also sound out some of the show's key players, very discreetly, about whether they might be interested in Mum's story, if the situation arose, and whether they would be sensitive to our concerns. We found out that *Australian Story* decides the content of its programs and retains all editorial control, but if Mum was up for it, then yes, they would be interested and yes they could understand our sensitivities. Although they made it clear that the program would be theirs, not 'ours', I felt that they had an approach to telling people's stories that would be sensitive and strong on the issues, and would support Mum's dignity without veering into a tabloid sensationalism that would be anathema to her.

In the conversations Wendy and I were having with Mum we discussed both the pros and cons, and made sure we really thrashed the issue out. We each felt that it would be a useful contribution for her to make, and we knew she had always found meaning and satisfaction in doing this. But we were both careful not to suggest that she was obliged to do it. It had to be absolutely her choice.

Mum was drawn to the idea of doing *Australian Story* if it really might be of any benefit to others. Although she'd had trouble previously with the idea of going public, it really was not in her core nature to run for long from problems or pain or suffering – either her own or other people's. And she was aware of, and disturbed about, the prevalence of the disease, and that so little seemed to be understood about it. She felt strongly that as well as destigmatising the disease it was critical to do anything possible to promote research that may help others in the future. If it would help for her to speak out, then she would speak out. Wendy and I said in no uncertain terms that we were confident it could be a positive input to the issues. Wendy spoke very movingly about how

Mum had made a difference in many ways throughout her life, and how going public about Alzheimer's truly could help promote social change and bring comfort to people living with the disease in the meantime, precisely because of the regard and affection in which she is held.

Mum talked through her own fears about being stigmatised. About how when she was a kid other children would point at somebody who was a bit old and senile and laugh and say, 'Silly old bugger, losing his marbles.' She couldn't bear the thought of being looked at and talked about like that. Wendy and I each said we thought it was true that going public was not without risks, but we thought the risks were probably not as great as Mum feared. Apart from anything else, people knew her. They knew what she stood for and what she'd achieved and they wouldn't call her a silly old bugger, because she wasn't one. Both of us said that we thought in fact people would probably respect her even more for doing this.

I also had to say to her that I felt that the people she was coming into contact with regularly could already detect some kind of problem, even if it just seemed like significant memory lapses, much more than Mum thought they could; that in a sense it would not be 'news' to them, and therefore would make little difference to how they regarded her. And that this was increasingly so, as time passed. Mum's reaction was, 'What!?' We had to talk it through with examples, and that was a confronting conversation, but I emphasised that although I was sure people could tell to some degree already,

I knew they didn't think any the worse of her because of it. They still wanted to do things with her, they still enjoyed her company and didn't see her as less of a person.

We had several of these conversations, and in each one we made sure we gave Mum plenty of space so that she could absorb what we were saying at her own speed, and think about it without feeling pressured. This process culminated in her decision that yes, she would do it if it would help. There was just one stumbling block in the end: she honestly did not think that it would make *that* much difference to anybody. It's that terminal modesty again! Wendy and I disagreed strongly with her on this. Mum listened to us and thought about it. I know how much regard she has for Wendy, so I wasn't surprised when she finally said, 'I think you're probably overrating the difference I could make but if you really think that it could be useful then yes, bugger it, I'll do it.'

Even after she'd decided, we talked about it again, just to make sure that she was consistently okay with the choice she'd made. When we saw she was, we went ahead with the arrangements that *Australian Story* wanted to put in place. We had one condition for participating, however: if Mum clearly changed her mind and vetoed it at any point, then it was all over.

We knew by now that *Australian Story* was finishing on air for the year at the beginning of November – just a few weeks away. It was then on a break until several months into 2004. We all felt that it was better to do it sooner rather than later. It meant Mum would have more meaningful participation in the program, and more appreciation of what happened afterwards if Wendy and I were right in our predictions about the way the news would be received. It had the added bonus of lessening our chances of the story leaking beforehand. But we had to move quickly.

CHAPTER 10

# An Australian Story

ANYONE WHO HAS NOT been involved in making a documentary would probably be amazed by the amount of work it takes. *Australian Story* is a 28-minute program, but it has high production values. Making it took just three intense weeks, with long days and nights for me and Sophie, who was helping me out, and even longer for producer Helen Grasswill and her team. There was archival material to trawl through, research to be done, and endless details to take care of. Helen spoke to Wendy and me for ideas on contributors to add to her own list, and arranged for their participation. Meanwhile we were working with Lewis Kaplan and Alzheimer's Australia to set up the Hazel Hawke Alzheimer's Research and Care Fund, liasing with the ABC-TV publicity department about how the release of the news would be handled, and looking after Mum during the concentrated demands the process made on her.

We deliberately started filming in a low-key fashion. Mum met Helen and the crew for the first time at home on a sunny spring day, and after talking with them was happy to start shooting on the spot. Filming continued throughout the three weeks, during which Helen was sensitive to Mum's needs in terms of trying to keep the filming sessions short, staggering them with rest days for Mum while she worked on other footage in between, and generally minimising noise and fuss as much as possible. Mum has done so much filming in her time that she knew what was required, and she knew that having to do things again and again to get them just right on camera is all part of it, although sometimes wearing. At one point the crew was filming her playing the piano and they kept asking her to do it 'just one more time'. She made a joke of it, but we could see she wanted it to end.

As well as finding the process itself very tiring she also found the subject matter draining. She was very guarded on film – although she was committed in principle by now to doing the show this did not translate to her being relaxed about it. I know that I was also frustrating for Helen to interview. I liked and trusted her from when I first I met her, so would open up to her off camera and then as soon as they started rolling I'd find myself clamming up, almost against my will. It was hard to let go of the ingrained habit of being protective of the family's privacy, especially around media. But it was more pronounced with Mum. And not surprisingly: this was the first time she had talked in public, to strangers and through them to the whole of Australia, about having Alzheimer's. I imagine it would be difficult for anyone to feel more personally exposed.

It became clear that she was not going to discuss the bleak or fearful or self-doubting aspects of her experience with the disease. No way. She was very chipper and upbeat when she was being interviewed. She focused on how she felt she was fine, and how it had not affected her too much. That wasn't contrived, she wasn't presenting a false picture. It's just how she had settled, by now, to seeing things. Helen respected that and worked with it; rather than confront Mum on camera and push her into edginess or distress, she chose to show other aspects of Mum's life through interviews with other people. Originally Ros and I were not going to be significant on-screen contributors – just part of the background and context. But as filming went on it became apparent that to present a fuller picture of what it was like to live with Alzheimer's we would need to speak at greater length about the realities of day-to-day life and some of the more challenging aspects of living with the disease. That way Mum still got to speak for herself with dignity and yet the show would not create the impression that the disease was a bed of roses, or insignificant in its effects. To do that would have been unconvincingly hollow, as well as insulting and disrespectful to other people living with it.

The day Mum was filmed with Professor Henry Brodaty was one of the ropier parts of shooting. Henry was interviewed for the show but Helen also planned to use footage of him and Mum talking together in his office, as they would during a medical consultation. (They had met twice before – once during the Canberra years when Mum opened a day-care centre for dementia patients, and once about 10 years ago when she had an appointment with him to check her recovery after the pituitary operation – although Mum did not remember either occasion.) So here she was, with a world expert on Alzheimer's at her disposal, and she could ask him questions and also give him 'her side of the story'. Every now and then she would say to him, 'I'm not this . . .' and 'They think that . . .', talking about how there was way more 'interference' in her life than she thought necessary. It was the only time during filming that we weren't either at her home or a quiet familiar setting – this was taking place in a small office full of lights and people and camera and sound, with all the delays and interruptions typical of filming. Given this, she was in a heightened state and her anxiety that day was particularly exposed. I wasn't surprised when Henry said later in his interview that what struck him about Mum was her fear.

Just like the rest of us, her moods went up and down over the days and weeks it took to make the show. When she was tired out or fed up, Mum would get irritable with the very notion of making it at all. 'Well, we'll see about this . . .' she'd say. But then we'd have a rest, talk it through, and she'd usually be fine to start again. Sometimes she would forget what it was we were doing, and we would remind her. I could only imagine how disconcerting that was for her. There are people everywhere, lights and cameras, someone dabbing make-up on your face, and then somebody telling you, seemingly for the first time, that you're in the middle of making a documentary about the fact that you've got Alzheimer's. 'I'm what?!'

When necessary, one of us would take Mum to a quiet spot and gently go through what was happening – re-prompt her about what we were doing overall, and where we were up to at that moment. She had a kind of multi-layered response: as if she was being told afresh, but somehow reminded at the same time. Not of anything she could immediately consciously recall, but something she knew she had known about before, threads of which would come back. Her sense of purpose would then return.

The air-date (3 November) meant that there was a very short period for editing once filming was over. Helen and the ABC team had to put it together in record time. It also meant a lot of quick work to set up the Hazel Hawke fund. To stimulate fundraising for Alzheimer's was always part of the general idea – the whole point of Mum's bravery in going public was to increase awareness and we knew that it was also a golden opportunity to help raise money for the cause. We had to think and talk through the various possible ways we could deal with this. Given that Alzheimer's Australia was already there, doing the great work that it does, we didn't want to reinvent the wheel, setting up something that would attempt to duplicate what they were already doing so well. This seemed wasteful and unnecessary given our own limited resources, our desire that the money be used effectively for the purposes for which it was given, and our developing regard for the work done by Alzheimer's Australia.

A separate organisation would have required its own administration and overheads and that would eat up money that could be going straight into care and research. We also really valued the fact that AA knows what people living with the disease really want and need much more than we could ever presume to: its helpline gets 24,000 calls a year. But we did want to make the best use of the personal identification Mum was bringing to the disease. We knew that some people touched by her story would be willing to show their support by giving money. We felt there should be some mechanism to ensure that money, given in Mum's name, was put to uses that reflected the priorities and passions of her life. The solution was to create the Hazel Hawke Alzheimer's Research and Care Fund and have it operate within Alzheimer's Australia.

We worked all this through, and started to set in place the mechanisms, including a website (www.hazelhawke.net.au), while the show was in preparation, and D-day loomed large. Or rather, A-day. *Australian Story* airs on a Monday night and we had agreed with the ABC that they would issue a media release announcing the program on the Sunday evening – in effect breaking the news that Mum had Alzheimer's. We, through Alzheimer's Australia, would issue one immediately afterwards, with a statement from Mum and a request that she not be approached for further interviews.

The ABC needed, of course, to promote the show, and would normally have done so over a longer lead time, but we all knew that the announcement of the show would unleash interest, and that other media would probably do their own stories on Mum, and on Alzheimer's, and that this could distract, in a sense, from the focus on Mum's own story as portrayed in *Australian Story*. While this was inevitable, to a degree, we felt that Mum had chosen to tell it her own way in *Australian Story*, and we should do what we could to ensure that this was the focus. That meant that we were all determined to do our best to ensure 'secrecy' was maintained until the embargo time of 7.00 pm on the Sunday night. This led to some rather awkward, and at times funny, conversations with a few rather mystified journalists and friends. Luckily they were nearly all extremely gracious about it when the news did finally break.

The ABC knew we'd be dealing with high public interest and reaction, so they arranged for us to have a courtesy viewing on the Sunday, at about the time they were also giving selected journalists a preview showing. Wendy and I, Ros and her partner, Terry, gathered to watch it. We didn't take Mum because at that stage, before we saw it, we weren't sure whether it would be a good idea to show it to her or not. Some of the people interviewed, especially Ros and Henry Brodaty, had spoken candidly about the more difficult sides of the experience. Although we had orginally assumed that of course Mum would see it, we had become worried that some parts of the show might be too distressing for her. She'd been so courageous in deciding to come out about Alzheimer's, we wanted to make sure she felt a sense of achievement rather than distress.

I felt my heart racing as the tape started. I had been there for most of the filming, and had seemingly endless conversations with Helen as she created the story, but had not seen any of the results as they were taking shape. That was Helen's domain. I'd developed so much regard for her professionalism and sensitivity that I wasn't too apprehensive about content, but there was nevertheless an acute sense of the risk Mum was taking, and that we were taking on her behalf, and you can't know the 'feel' of something until you see the finished product. Finally the tape started, but I could not expect, in that viewing, to fully absorb it. At this point I was mainly just hoping, desperately, that it was a show we could live with, that there was nothing that would cause us to regret this momentous step we were being presumptuous enough to take.

I was too close to it to be an objective viewer. It's strange enough to watch yourself and people you're close to on film, let alone talking so openly about something that we had fiercely kept so private. But I was able to register that Mum was coming across with dignity and authenticity. It was true to her. Any fears I'd harboured of 'tabloidism' or a demeaning pity were put to rest. In fact when the tape finished I felt awash with relief. We'd taken a leap of faith and trusted Helen to do Mum's story justice and I thought she'd done a great job. Now for the rest of the country . . .

On Sunday afternoon Mum left with Ros and Terry to spend time in a quiet spot where they sometimes went for short breaks. We thought it best that Mum be away when the story aired, and in the immediate aftermath. Our concerns were that somebody – journalists or people acting off their own bat – might track down Mum's address and come to the house. Or that, if she were out and about in her normal routine, people might be unintentionally insensitive in the way they talked to her about having Alzheimer's. It was better to give her a bit of distance, with loving support, while she was coming to terms with the fact that everyone now knew.

As planned, the ABC issued its media release on Sunday 2 November, in time for the next morning's papers. The release directed people to watch the show the next night for more detail and indicated that Mum would not be doing any interviews. Sophie, Ben and I sat down to watch the news that night (Jan was in Europe) and, flicking around, saw it had been picked up by the news on every channel. Being news reports, there wasn't a lot of emotion, but the tone was sombre and sympathetic. It was hard to sleep that night, but morning came at last and with it the beginning of the deluge. It is a surreal experience to pick up your regular newspaper from the front lawn and see yourself, your mother and your daughter pictured together on the front page. (The ABC had provided the shot, drawn from the *Australian Story* footage.) The other daily papers also gave the story prominence, and radio news and the TV morning shows were all covering it as well. The interview requests started coming in, via the ABC-TV publicity department. By the end of the day I'd talked to more than two dozen stations around the country. I did my best to avoid any extended comment on the issue, instead referring to a few key points we had made in our press release, and suggesting that the best thing people could do was to watch the show that night. Again, the response was sympathetic, with announcers and listeners expressing their admiration and concern for Mum. The emails also started coming in via the Hazel Hawke webpage, in response to the breaking news. People were overwhelmingly kind in their support and best wishes for Mum. We also started to receive messages from people she knew – some from people we hadn't heard of in ages. Without exception they were comforting of her and admiring of what she'd done.

The day raced by and by 8.00 pm I was sitting in front of the TV with the kids, a couple of their friends, some of my friends who had been very supportive and had known about the Alzheimer's for a while, and Lewis Kaplan. We breathed deeply as the show began. When it finished there was an odd silence; a brief pause, almost an anticlimax, while we wondered what lay ahead. Everyone agreed it was a sensitive, balanced program, and something Mum could be truly proud of. Meanwhile, Ros had also been watching the clock as air-time for the show approached and, seeing that Mum was in a calm and cheerful mood, had asked her if she'd like to watch it. She said yes, and so they watched it together. Mum had a giggle at some of the old footage of Dad, and thought the show overall was good. When I spoke to her on the phone I told her how proud of her I was. She was pleased with it all in a very matter-of-fact way. She concluded the conversation with an emphatic statement that has since become her mantra on the issue, 'Right. Now we've got to get on with removing stigma and raising money for research!'

The chance to pause after the show, however, was brief, as the post-show web forum began almost immediately. Lewis and I, Henry Brodaty and Helen Grasswill were all taking part and, with the help of a technician from the ABC, Lewis and I were soon online on computers in my home office. The response was huge and people were so kind, and so caring about Mum. This comment was typical:

> It was certainly courageous to present this story tonight. My father has been diagnosed recently, and I have learned a great deal in the past few months. But for such a public figure to come forward and seek money for research and help for carers is fabulous. She remains one of the wonderful Australians even with her illness.

There were hundreds more in that vein, as well as people seeking information and support. After a while Ben decided to join in, as a forum contributor, and took the opportunity to thank people for their good wishes and to express sympathy for others living with the disease. We were all immensely moved by people's messages. I was also, amidst the rapid-fire postings and responses of the web forum, experiencing another wave of relief. It was done – the cat was well and truly out of the bag, and we could not have hoped for a more heartfelt or positive set of reactions. Wendy and I had each felt that the reception to the news would be a sad but good one, and Mum had found that persuasive. It was her choice to do the show, but we had promoted the idea. And even though I had felt in my gut it was the right thing to do, there was never any guarantee about the outcome. It was a big gamble Mum had taken, and we on her behalf, but the reaction we were seeing so far from the media and the community was even better, and certainly bigger, than we had dared anticipate. Whew!

The wave just kept coming. In the days that followed, a media monitoring company registered 50 newspaper stories – taking in every national, metropolitan and major regional paper – many on the front page. There were dozens of letters to the editor, and follow-up magazine features. There were 476 radio items on the story, plus 129 TV pieces. It seemed that everyone in Australia heard the news and many of them cared. Many newspapers ran editorials as well as their news coverage, and they reflected the same emotions. Here are some quotes from five of those editorials:

> Hazel Hawke's decision to go public on her battle with Alzheimer's is an act of personal courage that has touched the hearts of millions of Australians . . . Mrs Hawke's gutsy

appearance achieved what money itself cannot: understanding.

Hazel Hawke's courageous decision to 'go public' about her battle with Alzheimer's disease will do a power of good . . . In once again taking the public into her trust, Mrs Hawke has shown her willingness to think of others at a most challenging stage in her life. Hazel, we can only applaud your courage . . .

Hazel Hawke's decision to go public about her Alzheimer's is in keeping with her life of courage . . .

If an individual could be held up as epitomising the values which Australians hold dear, Hazel Hawke would top many a list.

Hazel Hawke showed again last week why she is one of Australia's most loved public figures . . . her genuine concern for others, wonderful sense of humour and loyalty has earned the love and respect of people across the political divide.

~

THE OUTPOURING OF affection and appreciation and respect from all corners was so wonderful it was almost overwhelming. I was so proud of her, so proud to be her daughter. I've felt proud of Mum for most of my life – at core, that has nothing to do with what anyone else may think of her. But there is something powerful and humbling in the generous and whole-hearted embrace of her – her qualities, her ups and downs – by the people of the country she loves. And never more so than at this time. It looked like she was going to achieve just what she'd been dubious about, but hoped for: to offer a source of dignity, hope and comfort to people in the same situation, and to bring awareness and a motivation to help to those not otherwise touched by the disease. It was endlessly moving to hear again and again how much Mum had directly helped people. That has remained so, even though it has been a long time since the program went to air. In the weeks following, Wendy travelled a great deal throughout Australia on business and, as savvy and experienced in public life as she is, even she was surprised by the breadth and depth of people's responses, and tremendously moved by it.

In the days that followed the show, Mum's webpage received more and more emails. Every day I read through them, and every day I smiled and cried.

## CHAPTER 11

# 'Dear Hazel'

SOME OF THE EMAILS, cards and letters sent to Mum were brief, some lengthy. Some were from people whose lives had been touched by dementia, others from people who didn't know much about it. Some contained stories people hadn't told to anyone else. Many were so very sad.

Almost all of these messages, in their own ways, reinforced the view that Mum's decision to go public had been right (there were a small minority of rather strange messages; there always are with public figures). There were hundreds and hundreds of them, and to my regret we couldn't answer them individually, but we read them all and printed out those we felt Mum would enjoy, leaving them with her to re-read. (Given her memory loss, she got a fresh kick each time, whether she'd seen those particular messages before or not.) It was a poignant way of experiencing the upside of a public life: a sense of interconnection, the privilege of sharing something of the lives of so many, a sense of kinship and ties that intimately bind you with people who in a normal sense are complete strangers. I moved to tears over and over again, by the heartache and love and simple dignity in the stories people shared with us. They exposed an open vein of shared humanity – the richness, the grief, the joy, the humour the great and little things – the awe of which I hope never to forget.

Here's a selection of the messages people sent to Hazel:

Dear Hazel,
For many years I have admired your spirit, your courage and your wonderful humanity.

I am a 52 yr old man who really has little idea of what to write in a message such as this to someone I have never met, however I just want to tell you that I feel for you, I admire you greatly and my best wishes go to you and your loving family. May you continue to enjoy life and make music every day.

~

I have admired you as a woman of loyalty, conviction and obvious care and concern for others, including your family, over the many years of your public life and beyond.

I was touched by your tremendous courage and bravery in speaking out last night on Alzheimer's disease and felt deeply moved by you and your family's openness and honesty in talking about your feelings on 'Australian Story'. It was an unforgettable half hour of up and down emotions, laughter and joy one moment to sadness and despair the next.

Overwhelmingly, your story was an inspiration to me and I am sure to many people. I have a saying which has stuck in my mind, 'Remember Yesterday, Dream about Tomorrow, But Live Today' and you made me all the more determined to live each day to the fullest.

~

You have long been an inspiration to me personally – your life as a young mother and your determination to be there for your children despite some difficult times struck a chord with me, and with my life a parallel. Your will and determination to return as a mature age student to Uni inspired me to do the same, and subsequently graduate with a Bachelor of Psychology at the age of 50. Your biography was inspirational. Now I guess you face your greatest challenge. I wish you well, and I feel with your grit and determination and the support of your family you will give it your best shot. I admire you more than ever for your courage and honesty.

~

I wish to thank you for so bravely speaking out about Alzheimer's disease and raising public awareness. My mother in law has recently been diagnosed. Your positive words have helped her accept this condition and given all of our family great encouragement to help fight this battle with her.

~

I felt my heart was breaking as I watched your story. You have been an inspiration to me as I faced the problems in my life, divorce, drug addiction and death of a beloved son. As I watched you conduct your life with dignity and contribute to your community, I too was able to draw on inner strength in my life.

I am struggling at the moment with anger and resentment that this has happened to you who has always given so much. In my heart I know that we have no control over these things and that everything happens for a reason, we have no way of knowing what benefits our traumas may bring to the world. I send love and prayers to you and your family. I applaud your courage and sense of humour. YOU GO GIRL.

~

Congratulations on appearing on Australian Story. Over many years I have been in awe of everything you do – the way you have coped with all the setbacks which have been so public, your work for charities, musical accomplishments etc., etc. . . . the list goes on. In every instance you have held your head high, kept your sense of humour and become an Australian icon for women. I admire you enormously and, like many from all walks of life and no matter what political party, feel as though I know you personally. The country is behind you and we love you as our own.

~

My Dad has been diagnosed for three years and just cannot bring himself to tell his mates and old work colleagues. As a result he is gradually withdrawing and putting more pressure on himself and my Mum. I'm trying to use your example to get him to talk to people and let him realise that they will still be his mates and he has nothing to be ashamed of.

~

Thanks for having the courage to open up your heart and your whole family's life on TV tonight. This debilitating disease needs a much higher profile and now thankfully we will have just that!

My mother suffers from 'the Big A' as it will now forever be known (thanks to you!!) – and watching your program gave me permission to grieve again for the loss we are all experiencing (for her and for ourselves). I can only hope your future is kind to you.

~

Have just watched Australian Story and it made me cry. My father, a union boy from way back (gotta luv 'em), gave me your book for Christmas one year. I had it finished by Boxing Day, just fantastic reading. I am sorry I have not boosted your sales – I lend it to anyone and everyone. Hang in there.

My late mother was diagnosed with Alzheimer's some 20 years ago. It was so difficult for my sisters and I to obtain any assistance or information then as to what was happening to our talented, witty and attractive Mum. Now we five girls watch each other warily awaiting the first symptoms. Thank you so very much for drawing public attention to this illness.

A brave and wonderfully selfless act to go public with such a distressing illness. My Mum has been in a nursing home with dementia since 1998. She, like you are now, was a vibrant, intelligent, gregarious, loving person. A lifelong primary teacher with a love for the underdog and a vocabulary and capacity with language the like of which I have never otherwise seen.

She no longer knows me or my sister or her husband of 55 years. But she is at peace! The transition to that peace, as you have already partly experienced, was horrendous and the move into and out of a self-awareness of what was happening to her was terrifying for her and for her family. Sadly we only became aware of how long she had been suffering when it got to a very late stage and our understanding of dementia informed our hindsight. Of course she used her intelligence and her wit to dissemble and hide and to create a normality of her own. But peace did come and with the support of my Dad and her family and neighbours she got through that.

My Mum is my Mum forever in my memory and in those of all she knew and loved and touched. We all achieve immortality in that way – and you will too. I hope that your transition to peace is as comfortable and trouble-free as it can be. I offer my support to your family as they too will go through what I call a grieving without a death. I wish you and your family well as you confront the travails ahead.

Thank you so very much for having the courage to publicly disclose you have 'the big A'. My mother is 76 and has had the 'big A' for, we guess, about 7 years. While it has been very sad for my family to see her condition deteriorate somewhat over that time, we are still so lucky to have her with us and as part of our family. Big A patients still display love and affection and all we can do is to equally return that. Even though I suspect my mother does not really know who I am, she knows that I care, reflected in three simple words just the other evening: 'I love you'.

Your story is so similar to ours. Thank you for sharing it. We lost our precious mother twice to this disease – first when she was diagnosed at age 66 and again only last year when Mum passed away. Mum really admired you, now I know why. Our Mum was so brave, hardworking, generous, kind, loving, talented, fun . . . so precious to us. Just as you are to your beautiful family.

I wish for your family the strength and courage that they will need in the times ahead, but I also know that you would already have instilled these qualities in your children just as our Mum did in us. I wish you peace, Hazel. Thank you for your ever-generous spirit and contribution to the Australian people. I am so sorry that you have this disease. You and your family are in my thoughts. God bless you.

Thank you so much for being brave in the face of such a harrowing disease. Your courage gave me much comfort as my mother was diagnosed with Alzheimer's five years ago and now lives in residential care in England. I am so far away from her and can only see her once every two years. I try and ring but sometimes she is too distracted to reply with any coherency. Never a day goes by when I don't think of her alone in the nursing home with only my brother to visit once a month as he lives in another county. Seeing the love in your family's heart was so comforting and helped me to remember the good times as well as the bad times of her 'Big A'. You are a wonderful, courageous and inspiring woman.

Mum was my best friend and for the last nine years, since she was diagnosed with Alzheimer's, I hope I have been hers. It's been a long journey together with many tears.

The disease creeps slowly on and each stage brings with it decisions that have to be made. I hope, as will your own daughters, that I made the right ones for my mum at the right time, always made out of love and the need to preserve her safety and personal dignity.

As she nears the end of her journey I feel so privileged to have been with her. There were dark patches which are hardly remembered now because the absolute essence of her, her sense of humour, her love of people, her graciousness and that deep bond of love that we always shared, are so evidently still there.

I wanted to say how much I admired your selfless efforts to raise awareness of Alzheimer's by appearing on

Australian Story with your family. I found it very moving for a variety of reasons. I am the carer of a beloved grandmother with dementia and faced many difficulties along the way getting information, help etc.

I've been thinking all morning about what I could write to give you strength for what lies ahead. What I've learnt in the last six or so years is that dementia doesn't make us stop loving our family members – in a funny way it makes you love them even more. Regardless of everything that we've been through, my love for my grandmother grows stronger all the time. I firmly believe that while my grandmother is changing, she is and always will be herself – the same loving, affectionate, funny, music fan who loves dancing that she has been since my earliest memories. All that children and grandchildren who care for their families are doing is returning the love we were given so wholeheartedly. And that is the easiest, most natural gift of all.

~

I cried when I watched Australian Story. I cried for you, for your family and for me and my Mum. My Mum is 84 and her dementia became obvious about eight years ago. My Mum is a member of Mensa, was an artist, a writer, a gallery guide and an eccentric identity. When her short-term memory started to go no one told her she had dementia. She was a highly intelligent woman but I felt she wasn't aware of what was happening to her. Even when she became very disoriented, such as confusing night and day, she became frustrated but never said anything to anyone.

After falling over and breaking her hip 18 months ago she has not walked. In fact all she can do for herself now is feed herself. She needs total care. She still has an excellent vocabulary and her diction is perfect. Her sentences rarely make total sense but she is so happy. She still recognizes me but sometimes I wonder whether she thinks I am a carer. She is in a nursing home, is still feisty and brings great joy to the staff because she often adds her bit, often a lateral interpretation of a situation which doesn't make immediate sense.

I feel in the latter stages of her dementia she is happier than she has been for a long time. She was miserable I think for a few years because she didn't understand what was happening to her because she was never told, never diagnosed, never counselled. I think what you are doing is wonderfully brave but also really sensible.

What a wonderful lady you are to speak out about your illness. Australian Story brought tears to my eyes, remembering my dear old Mum with the same very cruel disease, who finally died from it in June 2001. I felt very much for your daughter Ros when she said the hardest thing will be the day when her mother looks at her and doesn't know who she is. Let me tell you when this happened to me it broke my heart into tiny little pieces.

Mum was also classed with 'wandering dementia' and also began to use swear words she would never have used before in her entire life. She would lash out and try and hit people, and even told me to get away and not come back as she didn't have a daughter. Can you begin to understand how this tears a person apart? Before this terrible affliction she was a very gentle and private person all her life. I sit and have little cries even now, when I think back at just how it changed her from my loving Mum into a person I didn't recognise any more.

I pray to God that the medical people will discover some sort of cure for this debilitating disease very soon. For not only the poor souls who are suffering but also for their loving families too. Good luck with all your wonderful work and hang in there. I'm sure you will fight this to the very end because of your strong will.

~

I am so glad someone has come out to speak about what the general public are afraid of. My grandmother has Alzheimer's. She has been such an independent and wonderful lady, and although we try to remember that, she can be so nasty at times. She says some hurtful things to my mother, like that she is adopted or that she is downright annoying. Mum knows that Nanna can't help what she is saying, but it doesn't stop her crying when she gets home.

Mum is there every day, trying to get her showered, trying to feed her. Nanna has wasted away despite our efforts and she is getting worse by the day. She is trialling a new drug at the moment, and although some days it does appear to be working, the bad days still outweigh the good ones at this stage.

Hazel, thank you so much for coming out and speaking about this otherwise unspoken disease.

~

I'm really proud of what you've done to help raise the profile of people living with Alzheimer's. My Mum, who's just turned 73, was diagnosed with Alzheimer's three years ago. It has changed her life a lot in some ways, but in other ways not at all. She's still as 'mad' as ever and when we celebrated her birthday she said she still felt the same as she did when she was 21.

I'm guessing it would have taken a lot of courage for you to speak out about a personal thing that you & your family are going through.

~

Our family has experienced Alzheimer's too. The one thing that will always be true is that you'll always be

Hazel. This I know for sure.

Well done for deciding to turn your situation into a positive. I would have expected no less of you. You're a champion!

~

You continue to shine as Australia's all-time greatest 'first lady'. Thanks for your courage in sharing your story with us all. I have no doubt this will bring much needed attention to this disease and to the families affected by it. And hopefully it will hasten the time when a cure will be found.

I was able to identify with your loving daughters having watched my mother display the beginnings of 'the big A' before her death earlier this year. I too was called a 'bossy boots'! And I think I have some understanding of your frustration and impatience with the interference the disease causes you in getting on with life – as this was very clear to me watching my Mum as she struggled with it.

My love and prayers are with you and I send my most sincere good wishes to your family for continued joy and laughter in sharing in your life.

~

Thank you for your courage in allowing Australia to know you have Alzheimer's. I admire you and your daughters so very much for the honesty in which you tackle this frightening situation.

I am also very envious too. You see, my mother has dementia and is quite advanced. She now lives in assisted accommodation which is no longer appropriate for her care and we are anxiously waiting for a placement in a secured nursing home for mum's safety. Unlike yourself, mum has never acknowledged or accepted that she has this disease, which has made it so much harder for my sister and myself to help her. Mum has fought us every step of the way; the closest she has ever come to admitting there is a problem was in the early days when she would say she had a selective memory.

My heart goes out to you and your family as you face the future. God bless you all.

I am on a personal journey with my mother who, at 60 was diagnosed with Alzheimer's. She is now 67. Of course we have had challenges – but doesn't everyone in life.

My Mum has been very fortunate in that she has a network of family and friends (and her ever-loving dog) who genuinely want to love and support her. Without this network our journey would be a very different one. With this love and support Mum's days have been full and enjoyable. Of course she has had bad days and good days, but we all do.

When I reflect on our journey I am grateful in some ways for what this set of circumstances has given to us. That is, it has forced us to look at our priorities, maximise the amount and quality of time we spend together and remember that we are all mortal and gifted with a limited time here on this earth.

Like you I work daily to realign people's perception of what it means to have Alzheimer's. I urge people not to pity Mum, but to admire her courage. I encourage people to spend time with her, to walk with her, to sing with her, to cuddle her and just look into her eyes and use love to calm any fears she has for her future.

I wish you well on your journey. I know that it will be a good journey as you are a strong person who seems to have put so much into life – you will reap the rewards of this.

Thank you for opening your world to the rest of us. Your daughters and their families are such a loving, generous bunch of people and it was great to see them working out how to best help you.

My Nana has the disease – she's 85 – she can still tell me in detail about the boat journey from Newcastle, England to Newcastle in Australia she took with her family when they emigrated – she was six years old. But she can't always remember me or my children.

I find it very distressing to visit her. She has had to move to a (lovely and really well run) nursing home, because she now needs sedation for her violent outbursts and constant care – but I have been encouraged by the ABC program to make sure I do keep visiting her.

I'll never get to have another game of Scrabble with her but I'm sure we can enjoy a bit more family history together.

~

I just wanted to thank you and tell you how encouraged I was by your story. My mother died of Alzheimer's disease at age 67 just last year. She was the rock in our family too. She taught us all the good values, humour and humanitarian characteristics we now have as adults.

I thought it was great to hear your thoughts on living with this awful disease and also very important to hear from your daughters. Thank you all for raising the profile of people with Alzheimer's, and their loved ones who clearly also suffer and face perhaps even more tremendous loss. There did come a point with Mum where it was harder and sadder for us than her. She was in good humour even toward the end, and there are many fantastic memories of us all laughing in unison. Her final Mother's Day was in hospital, and though not accepting water through a straw from the nurses she merrily downed a couple of champagnes in company of the family.

Toward the end inevitably she lost much of her personality but none of her compassion, warmth and dignity. We had many wonderful times in Mum's final three years and I can happily say we seized the opportunities for fun whenever they presented. I will steadfastly continue to support the cause.

Please know that your much admired and loved profile will make a huge difference in the lives of many.

~

I have been caring for my father for the last five years, since it became obvious that he was suffering from the disease. My father was still working in an executive position when the real problem was diagnosed. (Looking back, Dad was able to cover it up for some time.) I was thrust into his business affairs, in the end leaving my own just blossoming career. My brother and I were brought closer together (a good thing) as we tackled sometimes difficult decisions on Dad's behalf.

The journey continues. I have developed a really loving relationship with my father. He now lives in a lovely hostel and despite his illness, Dad has remained a real gentleman and I admire him greatly. He is of that generation who went through a Depression, war, educating himself post-war, always working hard for the family's sake.

Looking back I do wish I had more idea of what lay

ahead, and what the disease would mean not just for the sufferer of Alzheimer's but also for the close family carers.

Thank you, Hazel, for being willing to put aside your own personal fears about exposure to assist others who are facing a similar problem.

I hope you have been overwhelmed by letters, emails and faxes. I would like to let you and your family know how very much I admire you all for having the courage to talk on this very personal issue for you.

My mother had a combination of Alzheimer's and multi-infarct dementia and she died a year ago. The journey for her and us as a family was very difficult. It took three years to get a diagnosis from the time it was already very obvious to us that my mother had a serious problem. Services were available but trying to get them in place was frustrating and made unnecessarily complex by the ignorance and general lack of awareness of her GP and other medical people whose apathy still angers me. Just trying to get a geriatrician to come to the house so that we could get a diagnosis when we could not get her to go to a clinic was a battle with bureaucracy (and I work in the public health system).

I can only applaud your spirit, determination and honesty and wish you all well in the future.

Firstly let me say to you that I admire your courage, determination and perseverance. My mother who is 56 has Alzheimer's; it is now into its seventh year. In December 2000, after having looked after her at home for four years, against our want and will we decided to admit her into a nursing home. This was devastating to us, our mother was being taken away from us while she was still alive. She was never too sure that she had the disease, but when she was admitted into the nursing home she knew she didn't want to be there. The first night wasn't too good for Mum, as it wasn't for us. That first night she had to be tied up on a restraining chair and had bruises all over her wrists from the pressure of being tied up. When we saw her the next morning, our hearts were broken and tears fell so easily down our faces. It was hard when we left after seeing her and she'd follow us to the door, wanting to come with us, again it was heartbreaking.

Now it's been over two years that she's been in the current nursing home. She has settled in very well, and is quite active in the sense that she walks around a lot. She has lost a lot of weight and a lot of coordination. She needs to be fed, to be cleaned, to be showered and to be dressed. She is incapable of all the normal daily routines. She has lost almost all her ability to communicate, however she surprises us with a word every now and then. We aren't too sure if she recognises us, her family, but deep down we believe that she does, because her eyes and face light up as soon as she sees us. Memories of her from the past keep us going and keep us sane.

Hazel, I say to you, be strong and continue with life as if you didn't have Alzheimer's. Don't let it take over your life, but at the same time, don't fight it, go with the flow. Remember that you have a very loving & supportive family who will NEVER forget what you've done for them! They will now look after you, as we do with Mum, as you looked after them until now.

I believe that we underestimate what people with Alzheimer's deep down really know. I talk to Mum as if she wasn't ill because she deserves to know how I feel and how my life is going.

A mother can NEVER be replaced, she is the most important person in the world to me, and I am ever so thankful for everything she has done to make me the person I am today.

Good luck, Hazel, keep strong. To your family, I know exactly what you're feeling.

~

Thank you for sharing your story with Australia tonight. Can I please share my story with you, inspired by spending a beautiful afternoon with a relative who is also experiencing living with 'the big A':

It is the freshness of your face I first notice today when you open the door, more pronounced than when I last saw you and not at all spoilt by the smudges of earth across your cheeks. I can see you've been busy today and your eyes crinkle with happiness as we walk into the garden. You show me the pile of red and yellow leaves, picked up one by one and ordered into a bin nearby and there in your hair the last one clings so you look like a wood nymph. I like the way you leave your gumboots on while you make tea for me in the kitchen. You tell me today is a jumbly day while you boil the kettle three times and the cups and saucers cannot be arranged along with our conversation. It's a one-thing-at-a-time kind of a day and somebody's hidden the biscuits. I pour the hot water into the cups while you search for the stuff . . . in . . . that . . . tall white thing . . . and I watch as your hand reaches up plucking at the air for the words that are lost in this jumbly day, and then together we find the milk in the fridge for our tea. As we sip our tea at the dining table I look over and see you still wearing your face from the garden, then I realise it is not the fresh face of outdoors and gardening. I am looking at the face of where your mind is taking you, back to the young girl from yesterday. While our conversation continues I'm willing you to hold still. I want to capture the fleeting image of your young girl face in my mind and surround it in a frame, an oval frame of chestnut timber to match the colour of your hair and then I'll hang it in a special place in the corner of my mind. When tomorrow comes I will close my eyes and remember you, as you are today, at this very moment.

~

In 2000 I painted your portrait for the Archibald exhibition. It is now in the collection of the John Curtin Prime Ministerial Library in Perth. [This portrait appears in the photo section.]

There were many reasons I wanted to paint your portrait. Of course you were a hero of mine – the only 'first lady' in memory who ever tried to make that unique office count for something more than being an official hostess. You were compassionate, taking on the issues of the helpless and disadvantaged, making a real difference. You were honest and open, never shying away from disclosing personal hardships thus enabling us all to better understand and deal with our own battles in life. And so it is with your current challenge.

How does that saying go? 'As we sow, so shall we reap'? The love and compassion of millions of people that you have touched is with you now.

CHAPTER 12

# Out of the Closet

MUM WAS VERY PROTECTIVE of us when we were growing up. No matter how public or controversial a figure Dad cut in those years, she was determined to ensure we had as normal a childhood as possible. It was my turn to feel protective in the years between the onset of symptoms and the breaking of the story. It wasn't about hiding something I thought shameful. Not at all. It was simply about respecting her wish for privacy for however long it took her to come to terms with having Alzheimer's disease, and then to come to terms with what going public about it would mean for her. But when she had gone public, and done it so successfully, the relief for me was enormous. The effect on Mum was noticeable, too.

I saw this in a couple of public outings we made together not long after *Australian Story*. Before the first of these I was mildly apprehensive. We were going to a function organised by a company for whom Mum had previously done a little advertising. They had sent us a couple of lovely messages after Oz Story, and we were going to a small gathering they had arranged in order to present Mum with a contribution to the fund she had established. How would this be for her, I wondered? How much more of this 'up close and personal' was she able to manage? I needn't have worried. Mum sailed through, talking strongly to everyone who raised the topic of her Alzheimer's disease, and some who didn't, about how we must raise money for research. She was not at all embarrassed, and people were warm and gracious with her. And it was more comfortable for them, I think, than some previous occasions when the repetition or confusion characteristic of the disease manifested. Instead of people being a bit nonplussed or pretending they didn't notice, those things could now be understood and so did not 'get in the way'. Conversation just flowed gently and genuinely, albeit a bit circuitously at times.

Clearly, Mum was fine about *Australian Story* and its immediate aftermath, and she has become more relaxed and happy since the program went to air. As the disease progresses, there is a level of what is technically referred to as 'disinhibition' that often happens with the disease – in Mum's case this often, these days, manifests in a mischievous and rather wacky sense of humour, freely expressed. I think with going public her own acceptance of the disease has increased. And the *Australian Story* process helped that. She's 'out of the closet'. She's not hiding anything from anybody, not trying as desperately to 'pass' or to convince other people that she is okay. She can be open and be completely herself and I believe that has freed her up.

The notion that when you are no longer making such an effort to try to hide the real story from other people then you can be more at ease within yourself may be a bit of a cliché, but Mum's experience lends credence to it. I think that the disease itself doesn't hold quite as much dread for her now. Sharing her secret, as she did, has dimmed its power and dread a little. This easing has somehow made space which, among other things, has seen the return of Mum's sense of humour. Before, she rarely joked about the Alzheimer's, it was just too close to the bone. Generally, there are few subjects off limits for Mum's humour and now if she's in the right frame of mind she will 'crack black' about the disease, too. In April 2004 the *Australian Story* episode on Mum was awarded the peer-voted Most Outstanding Public Affairs Report Logie. It was a wonderful result for Helen Grasswill's team, and a vindication of Mum's leap of faith in making the show. When I first congratulated her on scoring an award she cracked me up with a typically Hazel joke in response: 'Hell of a bloody way to do it!'

The fact that going public about her condition has clearly helped so many people – and that they've let her know that directly – also has had a positive effect. She's never spoken specifically about it, because it's not like her to get puffed up. And anyhow she forgets she did it! But wanting to contribute, to do her bit to make the world a better place, is so deeply ingrained that you can see her brighten when we remind her of it, or convey some new message to her. Even now, every time we talk about it I reinforce it: 'Mum, you've done something really, really good. You've already helped a lot of people.' She invariably says in return, 'Yes, now we have to remove stigma and raise lots of money.' Even on her foggiest days she is absolutely clear about that.

It's also been wonderful to hear Alzheimer's Australia's Lewis Kaplan, Professor Henry Brodaty and others say they've seen the effects Mum's 'coming out' has had on people living with the disease. Lewis recently told us a wonderful story. Several years ago he conducted a training session for doctors, where quite a few of them said to him afterwards that they thought the work Alzheimer's Australia did was terrific but they didn't like the name and thought it should be changed. They said they hated to use 'that word' with their patients because it created so much fear. After *Australian Story* had aired, Lewis was at a medical conference where he told that story and the specialists who were attending it said, 'No, all that's changed since Hazel went public.'

Henry Brodaty says it has also made a big difference with the Alzheimer's patients he sees, particularly the fact that they could see that Mum's life was still full and happy. In fact, he describes the impact as enormous. It's not that we delude ourselves at all that it makes people's journey with the disease any less heart-rending. But to know that Mum has contributed in a small, positive way to that challenge is a great comfort.

Four weeks after the news broke, the Prime Minister, John Howard, announced that the Federal Government would give $250,000 to the Hazel Hawke Alzheimer's Research and Care Fund. The day of the announcement was Labor leader Simon Crean's last as Leader of the Opposition. Shortly after Mum went public Simon had written to the PM asking what help the Government could give, in recognition of the cause, Mum's history of community work, and the public reaction to her revelation. John Howard timed the announcement of the donation so that it came while Simon was still Leader of the Opposition, and he credited him publicly in the media release he issued about it. I was touched by the fact that Simon rang me not long after the announcement, in fact only a couple of hours after he had lost the leadership. It was no secret that Dad had campaigned hard for Kim Beazley to replace him (in the end Mark Latham got the job), and a more petty person might not have made the call. But Simon was reassuring about the affections of the Labor Party towards Mum, and spoke about his openness to facilitating anything that would support her or her newfound cause. He understood that we deeply appreciated the support, but were also committed to the building of non-partisan political support for the issues surrounding Alzheimer's.

In part, John Howard's media release quoted him saying of Mum, 'She is a figure of great respect in the Australian community; she is doing wonderful work despite her affliction and in that way, I think, encouraged other Australians to take a fairer, more understanding attitude to those of their fellow citizens who might suffer this ailment.' And, 'I know that all members of the House admire the courage that Mrs Hawke has displayed and will wish her well in her battle against this ailment that afflicts so many of our fellow Australians.' Mum and those of us close to the cause were certainly pleased with the donation – which we see as a good start! The next steps will be for the Government to consider adopting dementia as a national health priority, and to provide more money to fight the disease and improve life for those living with it.

Hundreds of individuals have also given money to the fund, and continue to do so. Many people who only just have enough money to get by on reached into their pockets. Some gave hundreds or thousands, but other people sent just a few dollars because that was all (sometimes more than) they could afford. Whether the donation was $5 or $5000, we were touched by it and greatly appreciated it. Since *Australian Story* we have not put any concerted effort into campaigning more widely for funds – that now lies ahead.

The manager of fundraising and development at Alzheimer's NSW, Marty Rhone (yes, *that* Marty Rhone, who we used to see being mobbed on TV's *Countdown*), says there is no doubt about the success of what Mum has done: 'Hazel Hawke's admission that she has dementia did one thing immediately. It significantly reduced the stigma associated with this awful mental condition, more so than any previous event or pronouncement in this country on the issue . . . the public has reacted not only with sympathy but with great admiration because of her selfless courage in wanting to assist others despite her own misfortune . . . It highlights the strength and influence that Hazel exerts.'

'Coming out' has had two other effects. One is to make practical arrangements for Mum much easier. For instance, I can do things now like go and talk to the local shopkeepers about the situation. They were always lovely to Mum when she wandered down there anyway, but now they know what's going on I can give them my contact numbers so that if they pick up on anything not being right, or see that Mum is distressed for some reason, they can just call me. Being able to be open in this way removes a large burden. It means that in a very practical way we can help Mum to be as safely independent as possible. And I think that this is another important reason to destigmatise Alzheimer's disease. Of course removing the stigma is better for the psychological wellbeing of people with the disease and their families. But it also allows for the easier introduction of practical, open arrangements that extend the network of care.

The other shift has been a slight expansion of Mum's social life. Before the news broke she had become much less active. She was spending more time alone at home, due to the reduction in her public engagements and because she'd stopped taking the initiative in calling friends to set up get-togethers. It was much more up to the other person to keep up the relationship, and of course not many people realised why she wasn't holding up her end of things, and most of them have busy lives of their own. So, quite understandably, things were tailing off. It hit a point where only those people who consciously realised what was going on – they'd picked up on it themselves or Mum had told them or I'd discussed it with them – would make the effort. They would ring her regularly and arrange things directly with her and then let Prue and I know so we could help her keep the appointment.

Once she went public, other old friends understood why the friendship had started to drift. A few people got back in contact to express their concern and good wishes and to arrange to go out with Mum again. Some of them now arrange things on their own initiative, but we have also assembled a diverse group of people who visit Mum, or accompany her on outings. We've nicknamed them the Concert Consorts, and we plan to develop this further. Prue keeps a schedule of concerts and other activities that might be of interest to Mum and when we get an invitation or we spot something we think she'll like, we check with her, and if she does want to go we find someone from the list who is free at that time. Prue will then make arrangements for pick-up and drop-off and so on, and we'll put it in Mum's diary and make sure she knows it's on. Then, on the day, off they go together. We do the behind-the-scenes organising and it happens fairly effortlessly from Mum's point of view. Everyone has a good time.

The other part of that is we can now be open and explicit about what Mum needs when she is out with someone. We will say, for example, 'If Mum goes to the loo while you're out somewhere don't just assume she'll find her way back to you.' We're able to openly explain to them now that if Mum comes out of the Ladies into an unfamiliar setting she won't necessarily know where she is, or won't perhaps immediately remember who she's there with. Being able to tell people things like that means that the circle of people with whom Mum can safely go out is wider and they also have a better time because they understand what's going on.

Jean-Paul Bell is one of the Concert Consorts. He has been a friend of the family for about 20 years. He is a performer – mime, drama, comedy – and in 1996 he co-founded the Humour Foundation, which operates the wonderful Clown Doctors program around Australia in hospitals and nursing homes (in fact they do a bit of work with people with dementia). Mum and Jean-Paul have always enjoyed each other's company and she is a big fan of his work. She was a founding co-patron of the Humour Foundation from 1996 to 2001. I asked him to share some of his thoughts about his friendship with Mum, and to describe what it's like when they go out together:

> I was in Canberra in the mid-80s and I ran into a friend who was helping out the Hawkes and she invited me

Hazel the schoolgirl in 1939.

A young woman with the world at her feet – Hazel at Northam in Western Australia, 1950.

Hazel and her mother, Edith Masterson, in 1947.

Hazel and Bob at their wedding on 3 March 1956.

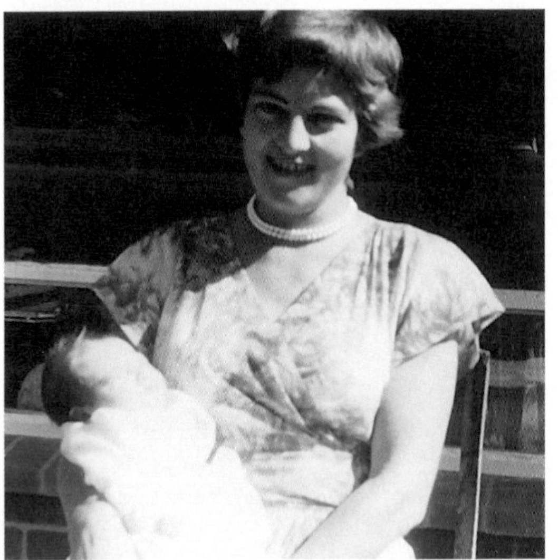

Hazel with me in 1957, soon after our first meeting!

ABOVE: Mothers and daughters – Hazel, me and Sophie in 1988.

RIGHT: Hazel with her great friend Wendy McCarthy in 1988.

Music has been a lifelong passion for Mum. Here, Bob congratulates her, along with fellow pianists Rebecca Chambers and Duncan Gifford, after a 1990 performance with the Sydney Symphony Orchestra. (© T. SCHRAMM)

Hazel at the construction site for the Northbridge house in 1992. It was originally intended to be the dream home she and Bob would share in their retirement years. (COURTESY OF OLIVER STREWE)

Life alone allowed Mum to do as she pleased. Here she is relaxing in style in 1996.

One of many new roles after leaving Canberra – participating in a ceremony in Newcastle as Chair of the Heritage Council. (COURTESY OF NEWCASTLE HERALD/FAIRFAXPHOTOS)

Reconciliation has long been a cause dear to Mum's heart. She was thrilled to be involved in the Sea of Hands event in Canberra in October 1997, with her good friend Lowitja O'Donoghue. (COURTESY OF MIKE BOWERS/FAIRFAXPHOTOS)

On 5 July 1999, a few weeks before her 70th birthday, Mum was invited to give the second John Curtin Prime Ministerial Library Anniversary Lecture. She was introduced by Gough Whitlam, who praised her contribution to Australian society. (COURTESY OF THE JOHN CURTIN PRIME MINISTERIAL LIBRARY)

Mum's speech at the Anniversary Lecture, called 'In Search of the Light on the Hill', was a persuasive argument for greater compassion, inclusion and fairness in Australian society. (COURTESY OF THE JOHN CURTIN PRIME MINISTERIAL LIBRARY)

ALP cover girl in December 1999.

Having a laugh with some local kids while filming in East Timor in February 2000.

ABOVE: Sally Robinson's portrait of Hazel now hangs in the John Curtin Prime Ministerial Library. (COURTESY OF SALLY ROBINSON)

RIGHT: 'She's a young spirit, a young soul' – Hazel with one of her oldest friends, Sue Spence, in November 2003.

over. I was a bit apprehensive; I'd never been to the Lodge. But I walked in, I think it was on a weekend, and Bob was in his Speedos by the pool, wandering round listening to the races and it just felt like a Melbourne suburban backyard.

I thought Hazel was fantastic. I've always liked her sense of humour. It's a very strong egalitarian Autralian sense of humour. I think that that sort of outgoing nature that she has and the free-range childhood she had and a very strong, loving family has held her in good stead all these years.

One of the best days I've had was babysitting Sophie and Paul and David at Kirribilli House [the PM's Sydney residence] in 1988 when Bob, Hazel, Sue and Ros had to go off with Charles and Di to the Opera House for all the ceremonies. I had a great time running around looking after the kids, and then in the evening we all went down to Admiralty House and watched the fireworks. Spectacular!

Another great day was the day Bob and Blanche [d'Alpuget] got married: we had this fantastic 'freedom' party for Hazel at the Northbridge house. There were heaps of people there. She was really quite high because she thrives on having people around. She's such a social person. She just glows, particularly in company, and she has this wonderful ability to make people feel equal to one another when she comes into a room. I still see that now when we go out together.

We went out recently to see the Sydney Symphony Orchestra, with which she has a long association, and it was a lovely evening. The taxi ride there was full of wonderment. She kept asking me, 'Where does electricity come from?', in the same way that a small child would ask because they presume all adults are all-knowing. So I thought hard and said 'I think all our power stations are coal-driven, Hazel.' 'How does that work?' 'I think it's that an awful lot of pressure goes down to a very, very narrow pipe and it hits a generator at the end and spins . . .' She liked that. Then a few minutes later, 'Look at those lights. Where does that come from? How did they make it?' I must've told her about 18 times, which was fine with me. I've got toddler grandchildren so I'm used to 'But why? But why?'

Then we got there and sat down. She really enjoyed the music, and at interval we went out and had a drink in an area the SSO had put aside for some of the invited guests. She loves to talk to people, it doesn't matter who it is. There's something about Hazel that makes everybody relax a bit. It was quite a formal crowd; we were talking to the Governor of NSW, Marie Bashir, and her attaché. She seemed a very nice and friendly woman anyway, but with Hazel any pomp and circumstance get ironed out. She had an almost schoolgirl camaraderie going on. 'Oh, that's a lovely top you're wearing', that kind of stuff.

At the end of a night like that she is definitely less focused, more confused about who's taking her home and that sort of thing. I think the whole thing's swimming around in her mind and she feels a bit insecure. But at the same time she is still on a sort of a high from being out with people. I really enjoy our time together.

CHAPTER 13

# 'What Nanna Would Want'

ALZHEIMER'S IS NOT A disease that children get, but it's certainly one that affects them. If someone in the family has the disease, usually a grandparent, then it touches them directly and indirectly. One of the things that I find most poignant about Mum's illness is that my children, especially Ben, didn't get the chance to know their grandmother well in her prime because they were very young. They've largely missed out on the dynamic, active, sharp, funny, all-there Hazel that I knew, and that a lot of Australians older than them feel they have known. For them, Mum tends to be their much loved but rather odd Nanna. They are very affectionate with her, they enjoy her and they think she's funny, but they have a perception of her character that's inevitably shaped by the disease.

One of the early senses of loss I experienced as Mum's dementia set in was the less hands-on role she was able to play as a grandparent. This was something she, and we, had very much looked forward to with her settling down in Sydney. She sometimes thought that she had been too busy during the Canberra years to do as much with the kids as she would have wished. As far as I was concerned, this was nonsense. She visited, we saw her often at Kirribilli House or the Lodge, and through her and Dad, Jan and the kids and I had all sorts of exposure to people and experiences that would not otherwise have happened. But Mum is terribly down to earth, committed to family life, and was eager to do all those sorts of little things that are so helpful as the kids grew older.

Being in Sydney, she was able to have the kids over for a meal, or pick them up from school occasionally if I was stuck working; get something from the shops for me – things like that. Little things, that you can take for granted till they start to come unstuck. She started to get confused about how to get to the school, or about the simple arrangements we had made. This was before we fully realised what was going on, but I began to see that it was a bit stressful for Mum to do things beyond her own domain, and that it was better not to ask some things of her, despite her willingness, so we slowly adjusted. The scope of things she did within the family gradually contracted, just as with everything else.

Of course my children are exceptionally lucky because Mum lived a public life, so through things like the ALP tribute dinner and *Australian Story* they get to see what she was like at her peak. It makes it real for them. And they get to understand the depth of affection that's out there for her. There is a lot about public life that can be intrusive and undesirable, but as Mum has always said, 'What you lose on the roundabout, you pick up on the swings,' and one of the welcome pluses is that it has enabled my kids to really appreciate who Mum is and who she's been. She's still their funny, lovely Nan but they fully understand now that she's also more than that. There are a lot of grandkids out there who don't have that opportunity.

As well as the direct effects, Alzheimer's can also have a major impact on children through the more subtle impact of the disease on the whole family: the grief, sadness, worry and anger involved, plus the time it takes up, and often the money worries it can cause. And they can feel the stigma that clings to the disease in our community. But with so much going on it can be easy to overlook exactly what the children in the family are experiencing. As parents, we often want to shelter our kids; not wrap them in cotton wool, but keep the worst of our fears and difficulties from them. But they usually pick up on them anyway. The older they get, the more likely they are to understand that we are in pain, even if they don't know the specifics. That's certainly been true for my family. I initially tried to keep the worst of my concerns from my children, although they came to realise that we were 'worried about Nan', as looking out for her gradually assumed more importance.

On the other hand I think their exposure to Mum's illness is all part of the mix. Life includes sadness and decline and loopy grandparents and all sorts of other deviations from some mythical picture-perfect 'norm'. To pretend otherwise is, perhaps, to be too caught up in some relatively modern Western notion of 'perfectibility': a 'white picket fence' idea of life that hides or denies the queasy, quirky, messy bits that may be awkward or uncomfortable, but are often, paradoxically, the sources of our deepest moments of connection. I think it's good for them to see the whole package as normal, and to learn to adapt to include it all. In February 2004 we moved to live next door to Mum, a terrific arrangement that makes it easy for Sophie and Ben to spend time with her. They can be good company for their grandmother and it's good for them, and for her.

The kids are wonderful with Mum. She lights up when she sees them – just as she does when she sees or talks about her other grandchildren – and they have each developed their own way of being with her as she is now and enjoying her company. One afternoon recently, when I returned home from shopping, Sophie was sitting at her desk with a quiet little smile on her face. When I asked her how her afternoon had been, she laughed, and told me she had spent it sitting on the patio drinking tea with Nanna. 'I'm so glad we're living here,' she said. 'I'm enjoying her more and more.'

When Ben took part in the internet forum that followed *Australian Story* he wrote that he was the one in the family who was in denial about Alzheimer's the longest. And fair enough, too: he wasn't even a teenager when Mum was diagnosed. But he seems to have figured things out as he's gone along, and now my sweet, prickly 15-year-old son has a lovely way of being with his Nan. He often pops next door to have a cup of tea with her, and during the time they spend together she talks to him about her memories. Always good memories, he says.

Sophie has made the cause of improving life for people with Alzheimer's and their families her own. In May 2004 she gathered all her courage and stepped up to the podium in front of more than a thousand paying guests at an Alzheimer's Australia fundraiser in Sydney and spoke from the heart about the effect the disease has had on her grandmother, and on her. I was so proud of her, and not a bit surprised to notice some of the people present wiping away tears when she had finished. Her perspective on her grandmother, the disease, and the effect it has had on our family is a valuable one and it is hers, not mine, so while I was working on this book I asked Sophie to talk directly about her experiences. This is what she has to say:

> Nanna was just Nanna. Which is a bit funny looking back, because some of my most distinct memories of time with her are from Kirribilli House and the Lodge. I remember yabbying with her in the little pond at the Lodge, and I remember one Easter when she went round and hid eggs for the grandchildren in the grounds of Kirribilli House.

She used to practise her golf on the top of the hill there and she used to let me put the pins in for her. Whenever all the grandkids were there together we used to roll down that hill. It was covered in itchy buffalo grass and afterwards Nanna would throw us all in the bath together with some anti-itch lotion. We used to love just being around Nanna.

When I was at primary school people would ask me, 'What's it like having famous grandparents?', but to me they weren't famous. They were just my grandparents, although they were extra-special because my other grandparents live overseas. Other people used to make a fuss sometimes. In the six years I was at high school there were some girls there who never got over the fact that I was Bob Hawke's granddaughter, and would even ask me to get his autograph. But there wasn't too much of that sort of thing.

It wasn't really until I went to the Labor Party tribute dinner for Nan [in August 1999] that it really hit me what she did and how much she is loved by other people. My memories of that night are vivid (and not just because it was the first time I ever went to the hairdresser to get my hair done!). There's always been love there, of course – she's my grandmother. But you really appreciate somebody in a different way when you see them in the way that other people see them. It's a different kind of respect and appreciation. That whole night was full of that kind of admiration and affection for her. It was a really good night. And it was a good time in her life to do it because she hadn't really slipped much then, so she could fully appreciate the gratitude that people were giving her.

I don't remember when I realised my grandmother had Alzheimer's. I wasn't a child when she was diagnosed but I wasn't an adult either. Kids get caught up in their own little world of school and girlfriends and boys and make-up and you don't really realise what's going on. It just seems like Grandma's getting old. I didn't have much idea of what Alzheimer's was, really. I just knew that it worried my Mum a lot. I was aware of the increasing anxiety within the family about her. But it didn't seem real outside the family. I'd picked up from Mum the habit of guarding things from the public eye and I felt I couldn't talk to my friends about what was happening.

As I started to get older I understood more of what was happening with Nanna. I also went through a stage of avoidance because she wasn't the best to be around for a while there. During that really angry stage Mum would pretty much have to kick my butt to get me to go and spend time with her. In fact, it was really only about two years ago that I fully understood how the disease has affected her and her lifestyle. You really do have to sit with her and spend some time with her day by day, week by week, to really see that change and the impact.

I didn't spend enough time with her early on to get the full realisation of what was going on.

It was really only once I started to drive that I developed a relationship of my own with my Grandma. Even though I was living very close, I was lazy and I didn't jump on my bike and cycle over. So I only saw her sometimes, when my parents saw her. But when I got my licence I started to take on more responsibility. Mum would ask me to call in, for instance, and give Nan her meds on the way home. I really became aware of how much she enjoyed spending time with me and I ended up getting into a routine of going round about once a week to visit her. That's when I started to realise that I offered her something that Mum and Ros didn't. I wasn't one of the people who were telling her that things weren't the same or trying to organise her. I just hung out with her.

I definitely saw the effect the disease was having on my parents. I could see Mum's sadness because she really knew and appreciated Hazel for what she was and the impact that she made on people. How intelligent, quick and on top of things she was. She was Mum's Mum and then that began to change, Mum went from being the daughter and getting advice from Hazel to managing Nanna. I couldn't even imagine what it would be like. Your Mum's always been there for you and then she starts slipping away. It was like somebody falling off the pedestal, in a way. A lot of grief.

Having seen what Mum's gone through has made me absolutely certain I don't want to have to go through it too. It's number one on my 'Don't Want To Do' list. I don't want either of my parents to get Alzheimer's. The grief of it is so clear when I contrast Mum's relationship with Bob to her relationship with Hazel – she still relies on him for guidance and for friendship as well, and he's still her father, still a father figure. Whereas the roles have been reversed with Mum and Hazel. And I really don't want to have to go through the long, long grief of losing a parent that way. My other great fear is that the children I plan to have will have to deal with me getting Alzheimer's. It's funny, I can't get my head around myself actually having it. Maybe I just feel too much of the young, invincible teenager! Yet the thought of my children having to experience that really scares me.

Dad was wonderful with Hazel during the angry, turbulent time, but then he always has been. There were moments when Nanna was angry at Mum but she would still listen to Dad because he doesn't get fussed. The Hawke family are very loud, very opinionated, very bossy, very turbulent and emotional people. It's not that Dad isn't emotional but he's very calm and very steady – he's very Belgian. Nanna was sort of no-nonsense, a lot less emotional than Mum and not as turbulent, and she was always like a pillar of strength for Dad. I saw him grieving for the loss of that.

During all this Ben was having trouble at school and I had my HSC. I was depressed for a while. And being a teenager is not easy. You get caught up in your own stuff and teenage girls are very self-centred. If I'd been older I would've been able to support my parents more. Even now I can't really imagine the hell they went through.

I think in a way we've never been a 'normal' family. We've never done things the way you were 'meant' to do them and I think that's one of the reasons why I've been able to adapt and deal with things. I think our family's great, the way we work. I see us as a functional dysfunctional family and that's helped me a lot. I really mean that. Things don't happen the way they're 'meant' to happen. Like John Lennon said, 'Life is what happens while you are busy making other plans.' You have to be able to just go with it. What's happened with Nanna was definitely not part of the plan. But it's happened and we all have to learn to adapt.

In May 2003 I went to Europe to see my other grandparents in Belgium and travelled around for five months. I'd worked and saved up for it and it was the adventure of a lifetime. At the end of it I thought I'd be leaving the excitement behind, but I arrived back the day before filming on *Australian Story* started. I jumped right in, taking on the job of being Mum's assistant. I loved what we were doing. I loved the idea of bringing good from something that had caused us so much grief over the years. It's what Nanna would want us to do.

It was really clear to me how much Nanna had slipped while I was away. Before I went she still had a grasp on the things she couldn't remember and it really frustrated her. She'd be trying to think of something and saying, 'I *know* this but it's lost . . .', and you could see her grinding her teeth about it. But by the time I got back in October she was sort of content. She'd lost track of how much the disease was affecting her, and that was a blessing.

During filming I really got a grip on balancing my actions with my Mum's in being around Nanna. Mum has to do so much organising and taking care of things, and sometimes she still gets frustrated with Nanna. But I found I could just sort of coax Nan along when she'd get grumpy and say, 'Why are we doing this? I don't need make-up on!', digging in her heels. Somehow I could usually just get her there, slowly.

The reaction to the show was fantastic. We kind of knew that this was going to be big but we never could've anticipated how big. The media coverage was huge and then the fan mail started coming in. It was my job to open it, and what people had written was so touching. I saw that Nanna was a vehicle for people to work through their own grief and people just wanted to tell their story. Nanna is so lucky in that she's got a house and she has enough support to live on her own. At her stage, most people would be in a nursing home. Lots of people aren't so lucky as she is, and have very sad and terrible stories, and I realised that for some people just being able to write in and tell their story was very healing.

I think the most moving letter I got was from an old man. He was in his 80s and he wrote in a really shaky script saying that he and his wife had always loved Hazel. His wife had Alzheimer's, and he'd been caring for her for 12 years and now he'd just been diagnosed with it too. He couldn't care for his wife anymore because he needed care, too. I was weeping reading this and then I saw that despite all this, and being on the pension, he'd sent a cheque for $500. Such amazing generosity. I'll never forget it. Nanna generated so much kindness and caring like that. And I got to see it first-hand. That was really special, something not many people my age would have experienced.

It made me determined to do what I could to help, in Grandma's name. So when Alzheimer's Australia approached me about the idea of speaking at their fundraiser from a grandchild's point of view I couldn't say no. I'd never known what nerves were till that night! But I got through it, and I was proud to do it for her.

Since the show went to air I've had a card from a girl I went to school with. I was really close to her for a few years but had lost contact. It turned out her grandfather had also had Alzheimer's for years. We were close friends during the time his condition was deteriorating, but I had no idea. Both of us were going through the same thing and we could have been supporting each other but we didn't know. It really brought home to me how important it is to get rid of the stigma around Alzheimer's.

It's been lovely seeing Nan around my friends now that she's 'out of the closet'. A little while ago I had some friends over – a group of about 10 of us sitting around talking in the workshop, which is a converted garage between Nanna's house and the main part of our house. And Nanna wandered over and stuck her head in, then came in to say hello. She looked a bit odd, as she sometimes does, hair sticking up. She trotted over and pointed to one of my friends and said, 'Boy, you've got great teeth!' (and he does). My friends just burst out laughing. No sooner had everyone stopped giggling about that than she went to stand near another friend who's almost 2 metres tall, he's huge, and she started pointing up and down to show their height difference. She has a disinhibition as part of the condition and she was performing for all my friends. It was the first time a lot of them had met her and I could see the warmth spreading around the room. Everybody fell in love with her in those few seconds.

I'm really enjoying spending time with her one on one as well. I pop over and we have a cup of tea. She asks me what I'm doing and I tell her about uni – she often doesn't really remember that I'm going to uni, that we've talked about it before – and she invariably says 'Really? That's good. I didn't get the chance to study uni when I was your age.' We have a conversation that is more or less the same every time. It goes something along the lines of her telling me how she loves the house. She loves being able to sit in the kitchen and look out to the yard and the front street. She loves having us next door. She loves to be able to go up to the shops and have coffee.

She tells me these things and I listen. One of the things that I've learnt is no matter what mood I'm in I've got to get over it and just be with her. Sometimes – in fact often – it's really hard to reinvent the same conversation over and over. But you just have to do it. You have to *want* to talk about that pot plant three times in a row and you've got to sound interested, as if you haven't heard it all before, otherwise Nan picks up something and that makes her feel bad.

We joke a lot. If she's in the right frame of mind we talk about the Alzheimer's, but in a jokey way. Sometimes I'll give her medication to her and say 'Got your lollies today, Nanna.' We do joke about 'the Big A' but I never force the issue because sometimes she does find it confronting and I don't want to confront her. I want to give her the space to just enjoy being how she is and not have to deal with any demons.

I don't know how the future is going to unfold but I do know that when it comes to Alzheimer's disease I want to make a difference, and I'm lucky because I can use Nanna to help me do it. As myself I'm just another uni student, but as Nanna's granddaughter I've got some things to say that people want to hear. These days, instead of being 'Bob Hawke's granddaughter', I'm 'Hazel Hawke's granddaughter'. That's fine with me.

CHAPTER 14

# The Same, but Different

AS WE ENTER THE second half of 2004, life for Mum still has texture, variety, light and shade to it. There is plenty of love and music and laughter with family and friends. She laughs a lot these days. She can still walk into a room and light it up. It's her familiar natural charm and ease with people, enhanced by a more recent disinhibition, which can be very endearing. As Sophie says, people just fall in love with her. I take great comfort in the fact that she is so clearly relaxed and happy most of the time. That's my touchstone.

I think some of this peace of mind is due to a partial coming to terms with the disease over time. Going public has also helped ease the demons a little. But mostly, I suspect, it's an effect of the disease itself. As the fog of Alzheimer's gets thicker, Mum's knowledge that she has the disease, and her awareness of its spreading effects, is less constant, less present.

Yet there is also undoubtedly loss. As the fog spreads, the sense of loss is mercifully less dominant, but sometimes I see it rise to the surface of her awareness, as she reaches for words to convey her sense that she is losing her grip on life. It's not merely the obvious manifestations, such as loss of memory or confusion. The disease has wrought a more subtle diminution of the nuances of Mum's character and expression. I don't know whether this flows solely from a decreasing ability to grasp and process complexities. It feels to me as if the steady progression of brain damage has an organic impact at the core of the individual, on their sense of who they are, on what we call 'personality'.

Mum sometimes, in what she calls her 'flat patches', talks poignantly of a sense of isolation, of disconnection. She is saddened by what she calls a 'loss of meaning'. Tonight I popped over before dinner to have a cup of tea with her, and she was a bit more maudlin and reflective than is often the case these days. We talked about why this may be. When I asked if she thought it was due to the Alzheimer's, she said, 'No, I think I just feel lonely sometimes, and a bit bored and useless. And I don't seem to have much initiative anymore.' She was also grappling with the realisation, lucid in this moment, that she is now dependent on other people to do many of the things she enjoys. It is hard for her to accept that it is now beyond her to set much in motion herself.

She did brighten momentarily when I reminded her that a lot of people feel that she is being very useful in contributing to community awareness of Alzheimer's, and that the friends who see her very much enjoy spending time with her. But then the effect of that faded too, and was forgotten. We agreed to talk further, later, about some of the things she might like to do, some of the people she may enjoy seeing again. I reassured her that we could help her, that there is still plenty to enjoy. Then we settled into a quiet, companionable silence.

Yes, Mum has lost a lot. Her short-term memory is pretty much gone, her visual and aural acuity is diminished and her organisational skills have largely disappeared. She is easily overwhelmed or flustered by anything complex or unfamilar. She is changed. But she's still Hazel. She's still interested in people and the world around her. She still enjoys company, and thrives on comfortable social interaction. Her basic values are intact and, on occasion, as strongly expressed as ever. Her sense of humour is still one of her most marked characteristics. She'll forget something that happened 30 seconds ago and then she'll come up with a sharp bit of word play and crack us all up.

One Sunday recently, Mum and I were heading to a birthday party for Prue, who as well as being Mum's PA is a family friend. The outing started with a discussion about what Mum had chosen to wear. When I popped over to remind her about the party and to let her know we were nearly ready to leave she had on a good dressy but casual outfit, just right for the occasion. But when I went back a few minutes later she'd changed into a suit, the kind she'd wear out to the first night of a symphony concert. It was one of the ever-narrowing range of clothes that she now feels right to 'go out' in. The top didn't match the suit jacket, plus there was a large stain on the skirt that she hadn't noticed. I lightly suggested she needed to get changed into weekend clothes, and whereas previously she might have been argumentative about it, she just went ahead and did it. She was mildly annoyed but not uncooperative.

So we set off. Driving with Mum these days can be very entertaining. She gives a running commentary of offbeat observations. She'll remark on things in the passing scenery: 'Look, there's my favourite lasiandra bush,' although we might be on a road that's new to both of us. Or she'll spot an elderly lady and say, 'Look at that old girl, waiting for the bus,' as if the woman were decades older than Mum herself.

Anyway, during this trip I lost count of how many times Mum said, 'Where are we going again, dear?' 'Prue's,' I'd say. 'What for?' 'It's her 60th birthday.' Five minutes later, 'Where are we going again, dear?' And then she'd remember that she had known and say, 'Damn, forgot. Tell me again.' It's about an hour and a half drive to Prue's house, so there was plenty of time to repeat the conversation. At one point we stopped at a petrol station and I went inside for some refreshments. When I got back to the car Mum was very pleased with herself because she'd remembered. 'We're off to Prue's birthday, right?' 'That's right.' 'And she's turning 60.' 'Yes.' Then a bit further along the road she said, 'We're going to Prue's.' 'Yep.'

'It's her birthday. How old is she?' ''Sixty.' 'Jesus!' she said, 'She'll be 61 by the time we get there!'

She loosened us all up at Ben's birthday party earlier in the year in a gloriously disinhibited moment. We were having a barbecue at my place for family and some of Ben's friends. Dad and Blanche were coming, but I'd thought perhaps it was more politic to arrange a 'split shift' so that they were here at a different time to Mum. But just as they arrived Mum started walking across the yard. I sent Sophie out to divert her while I welcomed them in but Mum kept coming. She'd forgotten the party was on; she was just coming to see us. Then, getting close enough to register the fact that there were other people around, she looked up and caught sight of Dad, who she hadn't seen for a long time. 'Oh my God,' she said, 'it's the Silver Bodgie!' There was a moment's pause, then we all dissolved into laughter, and went inside together for a pleasant afternoon.

Mum and I have lots of diary conversations these days. Now that we live next door to her, there is an easy coming and going between the two houses. She'll sometimes wander into our place a few times a day, diary in hand. The conversations always start, 'What day is it?' Once she knows that, she's right – she's got her schedule on the page in front of her so she knows if she's catching up with friends, or going to a concert or whatever. We'll go over the details of the arrangements and then she feels happy, in control again, and she'll wander off home. And then maybe she'll come back half an hour later, sorting it out again for herself. (I'm very grateful, at these times, that I've been working largely from home lately.)

She naps often these days, and a lot of the time we spend together is just gentle pottering, or having cups of tea with meandering conversation. Mum doesn't actively do a great deal in the garden anymore. It requires too much organisation and decision-making and too many things to remember and do in sequence. This showed with a grapefruit tree she bought, but didn't plant for the best part of a year. She kept moving it to different positions and talking about where she'd plant it, and then she finally put it in a completely unsuitable place where it is withering away. That would never have happened previously. But she still really enjoys being in the garden. We often sit together in her yard or mine, watching the wind in the trees, seeing what the birds are up to, or noticing the play of light at different times of day. Mum tells me stories about the various plants, and will segue into talking about the memories they stimulate. We watch the clouds, too. Although her conventional visual acuity is diminishing, her visual imagination can often be quite striking now. She'll see patterns and faces in the clouds, or in the swirls of the wood grain in her kitchen table. If there is a particularly beautiful sunset, she'll come in to fetch me, and we'll sit and watch the sky together while she tells me how lucky she is and how happy she is to be living here.

Her sense of social responsibility has been manifesting lately in her determination that she, and we, adhere strictly to the water restrictions currently in force. She has cut details of them out of the paper, and will tell me firmly what they are if she even sees me looking at a hose. She inspected the drip watering system I recently installed to preserve a beautiful stand of old azaleas, to satisfy herself that it was 'allowed'. It has prompted conversations about her memories of the times at our family home in Melbourne when she conscripted us kids into the 'bucket brigade' to keep alive her precious plants during an extended drought.

There is a real persistence and determination to keep trying that I hugely admire in Mum. I think it's a great measure of everyday courage, and it shows up in even the littlest things. Appreciating it helps me to enjoy those simple, commonplace moments together, and helps me to be patient despite the inevitable repetitive questioning and conversation that is part and parcel of Alzheimer's and can really get to you if you are tired. One recent public holiday we spent a few lovely hours together in my garden. It was a glorious autumn day, and I was clearing up mess from renovations and moving in while Mum was raking up leaves. She kept forgetting which bin to put the leaves in and I could see her sometimes getting a little bit flustered about it, but I matter of factly pointed out the right bin whenever she asked or whenever I saw her looking around with a pile in her hands. She just kept on going and after a while we started joking about it.

It sounds so mundane, I know, but to someone with moderate Alzheimer's a task like raking leaves up into the bin can be demanding, and I know that somebody else facing the same frustration might've given up. She didn't, and there was a sense of enjoyment and companionship in the joint endeavour. We looked around together at the end of the day, sharing the sense of a job well done.

Mum's persistence has carried her through a lot of tough times, and it's still in her. In terms of memory it's the long-term ones that are still accessible to her. And the ingrained habits. At one point during the raking she said, 'What time is it, love?' I told her, and a little later she said, 'I'll do this for another half-hour then I'm going in to watch *The World at Noon*.' Which is a show that she often watched until the ABC axed it late last year. That was an old memory that was still working, and had a feeling associated with being in the garden on a weekend, even if it wasn't actually Sunday and was way past noon.

Another little ritual is the washing. Mum scorns the clothes dryer during good weather, and has taken to removing any of my washing from the machine and hanging it to dry on her clothesline. It has led to some odd mix-ups (for instance, her holding up a tiny G-string of Sophie's and bemusedly querying Jan's new taste in underwear). It's a simple thing, but I love it: Mum gets to feel useful, we get to have lovely fresh-smelling clothes, and she and I have companionable moments hunting for pegs and discussing how much the kids have grown.

The great majority of the memories that seem most vivid for her, the ones she talks about the most, are the happy ones. Mum hasn't moved into being in the past, as some people with Alzheimer's do. But she certainly enjoys reminiscing about her childhood in Perth, which she has always recalled with joy – her family and the music, the bush and the beach. She's also lived a rich life since, full of experiences and people that she treasures and loves talking about. The details can be a bit wonky or mixed up sometimes now but she enjoys them anyhow, and they make great listening, even when you've heard them all before. Sometimes she'll tell a story I've never heard, and I'll wonder if in reaching back she has dredged up something previously unremembered, or if it is a phantom memory thrown up by the steady erosion of 'reality'; if she is creating a past where the boundaries between the real and the imagined are starting to disappear. (The same thing happens with recent events, too. Unless you were present to see something Mum is describing you don't know if it really happened, or how. In effect, the primary witness has become unreliable.)

There are some sad memories there too, of course, usually about her fourth baby, Robert, who died soon after birth. But she mentions him less lately, mostly focusing on the good times and funny stories. Just the other day she was telling a story about one of my nephews climbing a tree years ago at the Lodge and seeming to be stuck. The fire brigade was called, which was of course highly entertaining for a young boy, and by the time they got their ladders out, he'd climbed down the first tree and climbed way up another. In her telling of it, I felt that I was right back there with her, with her delight in the innocent mischief of the whole episode: 'What a hoot!', she chortled That's the kind of thing she remembers and really enjoys. I think it's a function of her nature, her inherent positivity and sense of fun. She has an incredibly generous view of people, and that stands her in good stead.

In terms of day-to-day life, Mum walks the kilometre or so up to the local shopping centre most days and often stops for a coffee. Although we have a cleaner come in fortnightly, she does much of her own basic housekeeping – tidying, washing, ironing and so on. Not as scrupulously as before, but she 'keeps her own house'. She reads. Not with continuity: reading a book front to back no longer happens. But she picks up books and puts them down and she reads the newspaper every day and reads garden magazines, and will clip an article for me that she'll think I'll like.

She spends a few days every so often staying with Ros and Terry at their place, or down the coast. She loves the time spent with them, the companionship and affection. She talks frequently of going to Perth to see family and friends there, and when we can manage the logistics she goes for a week or so and loves it.

She still plays the piano. It makes me smile whenever I hear it drifting in from next door. She's not as sharp or perfect in her playing as she was, but she's still better than most of us. She can still read music to some degree. Pieces that she knows she reads quite well, and although new pieces take longer than before, she can still take a good stab at them if they're not too complicated. And she'll play familiar tunes from memory. She grew up playing piano for sing-alongs in her neighbourhood so she'll play quite a lot of old ballads or union songs. I heard her belting out 'Solidarity Forever' and 'Click Go the Shears' the other day. She also still plays many of the classical pieces that have become entrenched favourites over the years.

I learned to play the flute a little when I was young, and Jean-Paul Bell can play the ukulele, so we've been talking about learning to play some of the songs Mum knows and going round and playing with her semi-regularly. We had the idea on Mother's Day, when we spent an hour and a half around the piano together, playing and singing old favourites. We dug out an old union songbook, and wore ourselves out singing them at the tops of our voices. I'm not sure how much fun it was for the neighbours, but we had a ball! A friend has also suggested a music teacher who can come round to Mum regularly and play with her, to replace the piano lessons that stopped when she was having trouble finding her way around in the car.

Music has always been particularly important to Mum, but I know from the reading I've done on Alzheimer's that it can be a wonderful thing for most people with the disease. Apparently this is because, first, music is pre-verbal – as a species we have been able to make some form of music for a lot longer than we've been able to string a sentence together – and second, music, unlike, for example, language, is processed by many different areas of the brain, and comprehension and enjoyment of it can often survive cerebral damage to more specific parts. I like the way the neurologist and author Oliver Sacks puts it. He says we listen to music with our muscles.

So I definitely want to ensure that now and in the future Mum has access to plenty of music: playing it while she can and listening to it. Another thing I've been thinking about in relation to this is whether Mum might enjoy sitting in on the odd church service. She grew up within the Congregational church and music was a very important part of it for her. She was a church organist and pianist and so the old hymns are deeply familiar to her. Things have changed in the church itself – the Congregational denomination is now part of the Uniting Church – and I'm not sure how big a part music plays or how many of the hymns would be the old ones. And Mum hasn't been a follower of organised religion for decades. But if we could find the right place, with the right feel, then I think Mum might really enjoy sitting there amid that atmosphere.

I try to stay on my toes in terms of gauging Mum's capacities and needs, and so does the rest of the family, because it can be risky to assume that things are the same now as they were even a month ago. I sometimes feel a bit mean and 'clinical', as if I'm pedantically tracking her decline, but apart from the fact that you can't help but be naturally attuned to the changes, there is also a safety aspect that makes it necessary. It's as if you become the silent watcher, noticing all sorts of details, not moving too hastily to interfere, but seeking to anticipate when you may need to make a change in the way you go about something. Sometimes, overly concerned, you can interfere too much too soon. At other times, determined to not intervene unnecessarily, you make the mistake of being too lax. It's a constant challenge.

Towards the end of 2003 Mum and I went to the osteopath we've been seeing for years. Since Mum no longer drives, I make regular appointments for times that we can go together. Sometimes in the past while we were there, one or the other of us would pop out to the shops around the corner, to get a coffee or post a letter, then come right back. On this particular day, as I went in to my appointment, I had an urge to ask Mum to stay put, but I dismissed it as 'worry-warting'. However when I came out of the treatment area a half-hour later, Mum was not in the waiting room. Oh-oh. I went straight around to the shops where I thought she would be, but there was no sign of her. I have to admit I started to feel panicky. I raced around in widening circles looking for her, but couldn't find any trace. The staff at the clinic were out helping to look too, and I rang Prue and Sophie to ask them to check her house and the local shops, in case she had found her way back home turf.

This was shortly before she 'went public', so my anxiety was heightened by the thought of how on earth we would handle asking others, maybe even the police, to help if we didn't soon find her. The conflicting voices in my head were getting louder: 'Don't be a panic merchant. She's gone for a coffee, forgotten she was going home with you, and will turn up in a taxi in her own sweet time. I'm sure she can still hail a taxi . . . Maybe, but what if something has happened, if she's fallen and hurt herself, is confused, is with god-knows-who going to god-knows-where?'

Mum turned up at home an hour or so later in a taxi. We had more or less given up on locating her anywhere near the osteopath's and were debating our next move, when she walked in saying, 'I've had a terrible time, I couldn't get a cab,' but otherwise quite unperturbed. '*You've* had a terrible time!' I thought to myself as my pulse went back down into double digits. I still don't know exactly what happened. My best guess is that she got distracted by something and then simply lost the thread, totally forgot she was out with me, became disoriented and kept going into an area that was now unfamiliar to her. When she did find a taxi to come home she had no problem remembering the address – that was firmly laid down in memory too long ago to be lost, thank heavens.

So another small line was crossed, and even in the familiar environment of the osteopath it is no longer a good idea to leave her vulnerable to wandering off and getting lost. I've spoken to the desk staff, and now if Mum gets up to leave before I have finished my appointment, they think of something to divert her – ask her to check a bill or an appointment, or make her a cup of tea. They are fond of her, and are happy to do whatever it takes. Besides, having all been involved in looking for her, and seeing my panic, they didn't take any persuading that we needed to be a little more vigilant!

Sometimes the changes, the losses, do hit me. There is

much to be glad of in Mum's life now and in her state of mind, and I am thankful for these things. I take great comfort in her good humour and peace. As I get over the early drama of the *idea* of Alzheimer's, I see that a lot of my sadness has come from simply being faced with the death of someone I love and the notion that I will lose who they have been, and fear of how that will unfold. But there is an easing that has come with facing the inevitable – bald as it may sound, we are all going to go somehow or another; and most of us have faced, or will at some time, the death of parents and others we love dearly. To get too caught up, for too long, in thinking that there is something 'wrong' with this particular journey is to exacerbate a simple grief.

So the drama has faded, to be replaced by a new, if at times rather weird, sense of 'normal'. I know further challenges lie ahead but, at least for now, life has resumed a routine feel, part of which involves adapting to whatever is needed day by day. While it is a relief for me I also feel that this more settled way of being is important to the quality of Mum's life.

But comforting as this acceptance is, it is not a complete inoculation against the sense of losing her. Every now and then something will sideswipe me with sadness. Some old files got unpacked the other day, and in walking past the desk I caught a glimpse of Mum's file containing copies of her old medical records. In her handwriting on the front is her Medicare number and private health insurance details and a bunch of other relevant details. The file has in it a lot of her own notes and correspondence. It triggered thoughts of how well organised and competent Mum always was. She ran her life, she ran the household, the family's finances, she organised everything and did it well.

This medical file was evidence of that, and yet right in the same file, in the recent entries, is the record of just how much has changed. I stopped and leafed through it and found a page on which, after her pituitary operation, she'd made a handwritten note: 'Memory improved but I need to sometimes retrace to recall small details'. I looked at the date – it was from 1994, almost 10 years earlier to the day.

CHAPTER 15

# 'Another Wonderful Legacy'

IF ONLY MUM WERE able to tell her own story of the journey with Alzheimer's. Sadly, though, the condition itself slowly limits the capacity to articulate experience, certainly as it progresses beyond its earlier manifestations. There is an all too resounding silence, a black hole in our understanding of the disease. Absent are the voices of those who live and die with it. I'm sure this has been reinforced by the fear and stigma the word evokes, by the diminished value we unthinkingly accord the 'sufferer'; all of which operate powerfully to push people's experience further into a private, inner world, thus depriving us of the best clues there may be to understanding and supporting them. Some people who have dementia have nevertheless bravely spoken and written publicly about it, although that is so far very rare. In 1998 former senior Australian public servant Christine Boden told her story of being diagnosed with Alzheimer's disease at age 46 in *Who Will I Be When I Die?* (At 49 Christine was rediagnosed with frontotemporal dementia.) In support groups and programs Alzheimer's Australia conducts, people with the disease are finding their own voices, sharing their strategies, and demanding that they not be seen merely through the filter of a diagnosis.

Mum has made it plain that her commitment to improving attitudes and options surrounding dementia does not, for her, take the form of personally 'getting out there' and publicly discussing the details and nuances of her private experience. While it is in her nature to be open about the issues, she is, in other ways, a very private person. We've had some funny conversations about this book, which boil down to 'What the heck! If you've got it, you might as well talk about it. I'm not up to it, but if you and Wendy think it might be useful, then go for it.' When I say that creating it has been confronting and sometimes distressing for me, so I figure she will probably hate the result, she vacillates. To shine a light on one person's journey with Alzheimer's is to expose not only their courage, but also the unravelling of many of the ways they have seen themselves. Sometimes she says she plans on 'vetting every word', and sometimes that she'd rather leave it to us. 'Why should I read it? I'm living it, my life's okay, and that's enough.'

So the decision to tell her story brings with it mixed feelings, and a sense of responsibility that seems impossible to fulfil –

I cannot pretend to stand in her shoes. This is inevitably only one perspective, and I'm very aware that it is only that – a personal, partial perspective, not a whole picture. Of course other people in Mum's life see her through the prism of their own relationship with her. To try to capture something of this, to round out the picture a little, I asked three of her friends and colleagues, Sue Spence, Ros Strong and Wendy McCarthy to reflect on their experiences with Mum.

~

SUE SPENCE IS ONE of Mum's longest-standing and most loved friends. They met in the 1970s when Sue was working at the Brotherhood of St Laurence in Melbourne. Sue lives in Melbourne still, and comes to see Mum in Sydney a couple of times a year.

**Sue Spence**:
When I first met her I thought she was Hazel Masterton – which of course, she was – but I had no idea who she was. It was only later on when she was going off on a trip and I said, 'Isn't she lucky to be going to New Zealand . . .' or wherever it was, and this other colleague said, 'Well, yes, but I wouldn't have her life for anything.' 'Oh, what do you mean?' 'Didn't you know? She's married to Bob Hawke . . .'

We just clicked straightaway. She was very interested in the same sorts of issues that I was – social justice issues.

Hazel was a volunteer at the Brotherhood of St Laurence and we worked together on a very innovative, unusual welfare project that involved the clients actually running the program. People working there either fitted in or they didn't, and Hazel was one of those people who absolutely fitted. She was able to work with the professionals and with people often coping with very complicated dysfunctional family situations who were making choices about whether they ate that week or paid the rent. It was a very exciting, dynamic, positive program and we absolutely loved it.

I knew her well by the time she had to make the decision about whether she was going to stick with Bob when he entered politics, and fortunately for all of us, for the country, she decided to. Then they moved to Canberra and she blossomed. All of a sudden instead of just a small group of friends and family telling her what a great person she was and how much she gave, suddenly there was this public response to her. People used to ask me what she was like and I'd say, 'What you see is what you get'. I know it's a hackneyed phrase but I think with Hazel it is absolutely true. It was just fantastic to see her have all those wonderful experiences, to contribute so much, but also, as she would say, get a lot back as well.

Bob used to say of Hazel and me, talking away, 'Punching out a few words, just a few million words . . .' We never lost touch. She would come and see me and my husband, Os, whenever she was in Melbourne, and I'd stay in 'my bedroom' at the Lodge and 'my bedroom' in Kirribilli. I still go past Kirribilli on the ferry and say, 'That's my room there.'

The first time I went up to Canberra to stay we went to the ballet and at the end of the performance we were invited to go backstage: 'The company would love to meet you, Mrs Hawke.' Hazel was worried that they might be too exhausted, wanted to be sure they weren't just being polite. The curtain was down, we went through the wings and on to the stage and I couldn't believe it, it was exactly as I'd seen it on the telly, just like the Queen going along the line. All the company was there, the principals all at the front, and Hazel walked along the line and shook hands with them and she just said to me, 'Follow me.' So I went along behind and I felt like Princess Margaret. I'm shaking these people's hands saying, 'Wonderful performance . . .' Following the Queen. And when we got to the end and went off she just looked at me and said, 'I knew I could take you anywhere.'

Much later there were occasions like the concerts where she appeared as guest pianist with the SSO at the Opera House. That was sensational. It was the Sydney Opera House and there she was sitting up there – it was brilliant! I went to one of those performances with Bob and he was so proud of her. He was just over the moon. She thoroughly enjoyed it but, typically Hazel, playing things down, self-effacing.

Then after the marriage split and her move to her own house there were very mixed emotions but I think one of the dominant feelings she had was a sense of relief. She loved her own house, right from the jump. During this time I went to functions with her on occasion, as I've always done. She was doing a great job. She was still enjoying it and still operating effectively and not having any great difficulties. It was about that time, though, that she started to complain about her memory. I didn't ever notice that it was terribly bad. We talked on the phone quite a lot and she was absolutely fine on the phone. But it did worry her. She saw it as more than just getting older and starting to lose her memory a bit.

In May 2001 she came to Melbourne for a function celebrating women in federal and state parliaments. People came from everywhere and it was wonderful. I sat with Haze and Paul Keating and Margaret Whitlam. They got all the parliamentarians up onto the stage and then Joan Kirner said, 'Now there are two other very special women here . . .', and got Margaret Whitlam and Hazel up on stage as well. The response to her was so wonderful. But that function is the first time I remember Sue or Prue ringing me and making sure that I was definitely available to go with her as we'd arranged. It was the first time that I realised the family were concerned that she wouldn't manage too well on her own.

The first time she spoke to me about the Alzheimer's she

rang me and we did all our usual catch-up about what was happening with work and family and friends and so on. And then she suddenly said to me, 'Actually, I have some bad news.' And she told me. It was typical of her that she was very philosophical about it: 'Bugger, I didn't expect this to happen but . . .' I felt it was so unfair that of all people, Hazel should have to bear this. I think it is a very difficult condition to live with. I knew instinctively that she would be strong and she would manage and she would end up doing something like calling it 'the Big A' and having that typical Hazel approach to it. But I thought it was so terribly unfair that she couldn't have a happy, out-there-enjoying-life old age. She'd got through the break-up of the marriage, she'd handled that really well, and found this gorgeous house and she was happy. And she's a young spirit, a young soul. I had visions of many, many years of us still gossiping and going out and having fun.

She talked to me about feeling very angry about it. I responded by saying, 'Well, of course. It's just so unfair, Hazel. I just can't believe it. What a bugger!' and she'd say, 'Yeah, isn't it a bloody bugger!' And then we'd go on to something else. It's never been an issue that she's wanted to go on about in great detail. If we talk about dates for me to come and see her she'll say, 'I'll check that out. It'll be in my diary. I write everything down.' Every now and then she will say, 'Oh, it's a bugger. I can't drive.' But then almost straight away she'll say, 'But of course

I'm so lucky to have my dear little house and family and friends.' She'll say, 'Sue's so good' and 'Stephen's wonderful' and 'Ros takes me out and we have such fun'. She'll refer to these things in the context of saying 'Aren't I lucky?'

When I see her now we're so pleased to see each other, we just start talking. She chats on particularly about old times – the '70s and the years in the Lodge. And that's really fun. It's as it has always been, a really positive, happy, meaningful kind of time that we have together. Her memory, particularly for the middle to early years of her life, is still remarkable. So we can still sit and talk for an hour. In the old days we could have spent the day and evening together and we would have had lunch and dinner and we would have never stopped talking, unless there was a concert or a ballet performance to interrupt us briefly! Now after about an hour I feel that she's having to work at it, which she shouldn't have to do and I don't want her to do. I think sitting around just talking can, after a while, be quite tiring for her because I think that she's conscious that her memory is quite bad and that's a bit of a strain. That is a big difference.

Another significant difference I suppose is that both of us focus on the positives; we no longer really have conversations about difficulties. Hazel might refer, briefly, to something that is happening with a friend or somebody in the family, but we don't talk about difficulties nearly as much as we used to. There were things in other people's lives that once she would have been involved in helping to resolve or organising – whatever the situation was – to make things better for them. I think that perhaps part of her not referring to issues that are sad or difficult is that at some point she realised she couldn't do that anymore.

Hazel is dealing with Alzheimer's in the way that she has dealt with what has been a very eventful life, as always, philosophically, but with lots of laughter. Very stylish – her own unique style. She's just managing it, dealing with it. And in a sense making it easy for everybody else. No drama. When I last saw her she talked about the impact of the Big A: how she has had to step back from public commitments because she just isn't able to fulfill them in the same way anymore, and needed to take responsibility for that. I was really moved by how sad it was to hear her talk about it and yet she said it with no hint of self-pity or bitterness. Typically she has shown courage and strength in making that hard decision and living this new, very different life with Alzheimer's.

I think our friendship will go on forever. And I'm sure that she has other friends who feel the same way. She's still very much herself. Her personality hasn't altered. She's still very much Haze.

~

ROS STRONG HEADED THE NSW Heritage Office and met Mum through her work on the Heritage Council. Ros was one of the key people whose accepting attitude and practical accommodations made it possible for Mum to go on working and contributing after her Alzheimer's disease started to make itself felt. They became friends and still go out regularly to concerts.

**Ros Strong**:
I met Hazel through the Heritage Council. I was the acting director of the NSW Heritage Office when Hazel joined the council. She was only the third chair in the council's 20-year history, and she was appointed with the idea of making it a more community-related organisation. I stayed on as director and got to work with her and see her in action. And she was absolutely fabulous.

She chaired about three meetings before we came to another arrangement at her request. It wasn't something she did particularly well or felt particularly happy about, so her deputy took that over for her. But her other work with the council was just marvellous. People just came up and talked to her all the time, anywhere. I'd be walking out to get onto a plane with her, and it was usually a country plane so we'd be walking across the tarmac, and suddenly it'd be 'Where's Hazel?' So you'd stop and there she'd be, having the most engaged conversation with somebody who'd just come up and said, 'Hi Hazel, I'd love to talk to you.' Or we'd be on a Cobb & Co coach clop-clop-clopping up and down the streets in Tenterfield at 8.00 am on the way to a breakfast at the Tenterfield railway station and somebody would say, 'Hi Hazel! Read your book!' It was super, she was so engaging in that role. We became friends too and we'd often go to concerts together.

It was probably about 1999 that I started to notice that something was going on. Hazel didn't always know what was happening next. I remember one time we were in the city together for work and she needed to stop in at a Chinese herbalist which she said was 'just down here'. We started walking and it turned out to be an awfully long way and she wasn't really sure where she was going. Now you could put that down to the fact that she'd lived in Perth, Canberra, Melbourne, Sydney – all over. But I wondered. And when we went out together it started to be that she would ask me about Tony, my husband, and then she'd ask me again.

I had an outstanding executive assistant called Christine Marks and she really made a job of looking after Hazel. She did a running sheet or order of events that was easy, and Hazel always referred to that; she could rely on it. She'd read it and she'd know where she was, but otherwise she'd be surprised. Christine, and Murray Brown, who was working with us in public relations, and I all planned around it. We didn't really talk about it.

Towards the end of Hazel's period on the council one of us would accompany her to every event and make sure she was all right. I know there was one speech she gave to the Council of the Ageing, I wasn't able to be there but Murray and Christine were there, and it must have been about the time she was diagnosed. She wasn't sure that she wanted to go ahead with it. She didn't know what she was going to do – she couldn't remember what had just been said to her about it. But she gave the speech and it was fabulous. She related to all the people in that room. And none of them knew. She could still deliver a speech and as long as she was supported by people from the office she could feel confident, even though she wasn't sure quite what was happening. She'd give a speech and she could have a conversation with anybody afterwards and they wouldn't have known that there was any issue.

We certainly did support her, but she was such a gift, you see. You just had to think well, gosh, we should make the most of this. So we probably exploited her as well as supporting her, because she shone a light on heritage, and connected people to us in a way that we couldn't possibly have done with anybody else.

I remember after she'd been diagnosed, she was cross, extremely cross with Sue and Ros for having 'forced her' to have the diagnosis. She knew that they cared for her but she didn't feel that had added value, at that time. She was cross for quite a while. She felt that it meant something had been taken away from her. She was sad about it, and she wasn't sure what would happen down the track.

Now when we go out it's usually to a concert. I'm pleased to see her whenever I see her, and she seems pleased to see me. Now that one knows about the disease in a more public and explicit way, you're sort of pleased that she still knows who you are. If I come and pick her up we might have the same series of questions several times in the journey. But at the same time, she can talk about when she did X or Y with the Heritage Council, or further back. If we're going to something by the Australian Chamber Orchestra she'll tell me the story about how Richard Tognetti's mother contacted her when she was the prime minister's wife and asked her for her help, and she'll tell me the whole story again about Richard and his violin. She'd told it to me once and then she hadn't told me again for quite a while, but now she'll tell me every time we go to the ACO.

Like many of her friends, perhaps, I should spend more time with her. It's probably a little bit of an effort but it's not a terrible burden. It's just a matter of wanting to be sure that everything's okay for her. For instance if I go to an ACO concert with just my husband, then there's any number of people we'll chat to at interval. But if we go with Hazel, we won't go flutter, flutter, flutter around the room. We want to make sure it's a stable sort of encounter for her and not troubling.

Alzheimer's afflicts people in different ways but Hazel just seems to be able to continue in certain dimensions of her life. If we're at a concert she absorbs the music and loves the atmosphere and is pleased to be there. She always knows someone in the audience, and of course the audience knows her. Her social interaction skills are still pretty strong. She still really engages with people.

~

WENDY MCCARTHY IS SOMEONE Mum trusts implicitly and admires enormously. They have been friends for more than two decades. The degree to which they share deeply embedded values and interests is striking, and has only grown over time. Wendy is one of the 'beacons' Mum looks to for wise counsel as well as dear friendship.

**Wendy McCarthy**:
I first met Hazel around 1978 or '79. I was on the National Women's Advisory Council and one of my colleagues there was Jan Marsh, who knew Hazel and Bob. Jan introduced us and it was quite interesting really, because I was a bit in awe of Hazel and she was a bit in awe of me. She thought I was this kind of outspoken, brave feminist and I thought she was this super cool woman who was managing fairly difficult family circumstances. We clicked even then.

I met Hazel a few more times in the next few years, then in 1987, when I was working for the Australian Bicentennial Authority, the Sydney Symphony Orchestra was invited as part of the Bicentennial celebrations to perform in New York at the UN. Mary Vallentine, who was the managing director of the SSO, asked me if I'd like to go and act as the communications and marketing director on tour. I thought it was a fantastic idea and I suggested asking Hazel to come along too. I knew she loved the orchestra, and she was the prime minister's wife and those sort of positions matter in the States. I rang up the Department of Prime Minister and Cabinet and they said, 'No way. There's no precedent.' I remember distinctly it was a Friday and I said, 'I think by Monday lunchtime you will be able to find a precedent and if you couldn't, I'm sure I could.' They went away and by Monday they had found a precedent. So off we went on this trip – our 'gig with the band'.

It was fantastic. We had the best time that you could possibly imagine together. And we became really firm friends. We went and had lunch with the rich women in New York and visited the Consul General and we made sure we chatted up people in the audience. We had a wonderful time, running around throwing pixie dust and music on everyone. At that time Bob was quite surprised at how significant a public figure Hazel had become. And in a way the orchestra tour demonstrated that better than any other thing because she did it in a foreign place just as well as she was doing it at home.

Having met her when I did, I saw Hazel emerging as a contemporary woman with a whole new set of educational skills, whose confidence was growing and taking her through to her prime. The thing I really admired so much about her then is that she took to a whole new phase of life like a woman of 25. She had a career, she changed the way she looked; she reinvented herself, in a way, and did it so successfully. There are very few people I know who can do that, let alone do it with grace, and not run the risk of alienating all the people they've gone through life with. And that is one of Hazel's enduring charms. I don't think she ever loses a friend or a supporter.

When I think about Hazel in her professional prime there are certain words that come to mind. Commitment, for one. Whatever she does, she commits to it totally. Integrity is another: she always brings integrity to whatever she's doing and she wouldn't take on something if it wasn't possible for her to retain her integrity. Inclusiveness, too. She's extremely good at taking along a lot of people and making sure they feel included – they get to be in the sunshine of her passion. And, oddly enough, humility: she never actually thinks that she's good enough to do something and she's totally surprised – every time – when people say to her how good she is at it. She says, 'You think so? Oh.' It's so endearing.

She applies all of these qualities to her friendships, too, and the other thing is that she is extraordinarily loyal. I can't imagine what heinous thing you would have to do to stop Hazel being loyal to you, because she just assumes the best of you and that's a very big thing to do. She would always assume the best rather than the worst.

Around the end of 1995, when I was chairing the national Heritage Commission, Craig Knowles, then the NSW Minister for Urban Affairs and Planning, had asked me what I thought about Hazel becoming chair of the NSW Heritage Council. I thought it was a terrific idea and I spoke with Hazel. She said to me, 'I don't really want to chair the meetings because I think I'm having a lot of trouble with my memory.' I kind of jollied her out of it and said, 'No, no, you'll be fine.' When she'd been in hospital having the pituitary operation I was conscious of the fact that people were concerned about memory loss. And after the operation Hazel said she was less confident about her memory than she had been before. I could see no difference, and I told her that. But she said 'I'm not good with chairing meetings. I'm not experienced at it and I have a bit of trouble remembering all the bits and pieces.' Well, chairing things is complex. It's just not a skill that everybody has; some very bright people who don't have memory problems can't chair things. So, fine.

It was only at my 60th birthday party, in July 2001, that I began to realise something was going on. I suppose I was in denial really, before that, because people had said to me, 'I think she's having some memory problems,' and I said, 'No, no, no. Rubbish.' But at the birthday party I really noticed it very strongly because of a conversation she had with Sam, my younger son. She's known him virtually his whole life and always liked him, and about three times during lunch she said to Sam, 'Have I met you?' Sam, who's a healthcare worker, came up to me and said, 'Mum, you don't realise. Hazel has lost it. She's having a lot of trouble focusing.'

This did worry me, but not as much as you might think. It wasn't as if she didn't recognise Sam, it's just that she'd forget who he was in between times during the course of the conversation. There are lots of times in life when you're under stress and you forget things, and as people get older they do have short-term memory loss and get a bit muddled about things. After that conversation with Sam I did have a kind of amber light in my head, to make sure that Hazel wasn't exposed or in a position that was difficult for her, however that's a courtesy I would extend to many people.

Then when the diagnosis was made and Sue came and told me I felt my stomach falling out on the floor. Empty, gone. And then I felt really angry. I just was furious – absolutely furious. I thought, Damn! How unfair is that?

And then I felt sadness that Hazel's horizons were being curtailed. And I felt concerned about how much she might curtail them more than she needed to, and how much she might need to – both of which are unknown.

I decided that I would not raise the diagnosis with her; I'd leave it for her to raise with me. I gave her plenty of space to talk about it. I think it was a year before she said that she'd had a few tests done – 'Sue had this silly idea' that she should have a few tests – and that it was a real bummer, but the disease was only at a mild stage, and life was going to go on. And gradually she then started to talk a bit about it. One day over lunch with a couple of other really close friends she said, 'Well, I just have to watch what I do, and there are a few things I can't do, but by and large it's okay.' She was taking a fairly stoic view of it at that stage.

A few times when she'd talk about it she'd say, 'It just makes me so angry . . .' And then around a year or so ago when we were having a reconsideration of some of her financial and practical affairs I saw a lot of anger in her, because she felt she was losing control over her life. She didn't want to be, in a sense, an accomplice in organising other people to manage her affairs. She wanted to manage them herself. And yet she didn't want to fully manage them herself; she wanted other people to have Power of Attorney and so on. I could see anger and anxiety then. Otherwise I didn't really see her anger until we were talking about making *Australian Story*.

I'd been talking with Sue in general about when things would become public and how the family would manage it. There was a bit of gossip around about what was really wrong with Hazel. Just because she was no longer as visible as she'd been. A couple of very concerned people who care a great deal for her said, 'I hear she's not that well. How is she?' A couple of people were even mentioning Alzheimer's. I just hopped around the issue, and said, 'Oh, I don't know that that's the best diagnosis. I think she's got some short-term memory loss . . .' Then Barbara Cail rang me up. I've known Barbara for a very long time and I knew she was on the board of Alzheimer's Australia but I wasn't even thinking about that organisation in the context of Hazel. It turned out she had heard the rumours but at the time she just said, 'Look, I've just got this idea. Why don't we think about Hazel being the spokesperson for Alzheimer's Australia?'

I thought it was a brilliant idea because it would present the opportunity for Hazel to include the community, and to demonstrate her commitment, compassion and integrity – all the things that she has always had when she's worked on any cause. And it offered her an opportunity to have as much control as she could in making her own statement.

But even though I thought it was a good idea, I did have concerns. It's very rare that I don't sleep, but I had a few sleepless nights then examining my conscience. In fact when Barbara suggested it to me, I wrestled with it for two weeks before I raised it with Sue. I did sound Hazel out one on one and she said she thought that if I thought it was a good idea, and I thought she could be useful in helping people come to terms with it, then it would be a reasonable thing to do. Then I spoke to her on the phone a couple of times and she said, 'I'm not sure that I want that label on me but you know, I'm still thinking about it.' It was during this time that I also saw her anger again. The idea was confronting: 'If I'm going public, it means I have to bloody-well acknowledge that I've got this damn thing. There's no other road once I take this label.' That anger would rise and fall constantly.

A couple of weeks after I first spoke about it with Hazel, she and Sue and I sat down and talked it through. Hazel would say, 'It's only the car I've had to give up, what difference does it make?' And then she'd think about it and say, 'Do you think I should?' It was a struggle for her to come to terms with her self-consciousness, the humiliation, the fear, the embarrassment. The fear that by doing it she'd put herself in another place forever. We went around the block 40 times. Then she said, 'Oh, if you think it's a good thing, we'll give it a burl.'

So then I had a few more sleepless nights. First of all about the fact that I had the audacity to ask Hazel to do it. And second, if it turned out to be damaging I would have to accept responsibility. There were real risks. She might have been humiliated. It might have been so stressful it accelerated the disease – I didn't know enough about it to know whether that was possible but I know stress does strange things to people. It might have been interpreted in the wrong way – as attention-seeking or publicity-grabbing or whatever. I just kept thinking about what the risks could be and whether the benefits could outweigh the risks. And I felt they would.

I thought the finished show was fantastic, an extraordinarily courageous and powerful piece of television from everyone who was a part of it. As for the way it was received, I was truly astonished at the media interest. It's a long time since I've seen one person on *Australian Story* on the front page of every major metropolitan and national newspaper.

About four weeks after the show was on air we went to a concert together. It was the first time she'd been out in that kind of public arena since she'd done the show and a stranger came up to her at interval and said, 'Hazel, oh I hope I can call you that, oh, um, Mrs Hawke . . .' And Hazel said, 'Oh don't call me that, call me Hazel.' And the woman said, 'I just want to tell you how wonderful it was that you did that show. It was absolutely fantastic and marvellous . . .' And more in that vein. Hazel said, 'Well!', pointing to me, 'Mrs Bossy Boots made me do it.' There I am, feeling like Princess Machiavelli, and thinking, 'Oh dear, are we about to have an Alzheimer's moment!' Hazel went on, 'She just said to me, "You have to do it." But I'm really glad I did, and you know why? I feel so light. I just feel so light, because I don't have to hide it any more.' And this woman just looked at Hazel and said, 'Well that's wonderful because we'd like to share the load with you.'

And for me, that reaction of Hazel's is what it was all about. If she feels lighter now rather than heavy with that label, well I'm very happy.

IT WOULD HAVE BEEN nice to finish on that note, but just a few days ago I spent time with Hazel for the first time in a while, and I saw the effects of the disease in a way I hadn't before.

I went to her place in the evening and she was really, really thrilled to see me. She was on the phone to Ros when I arrived, and after I'd said hello to Ros, Hazel said to her, 'I can't talk to you now, Wendy and I are going to sit down and have a really good gasbag.' We organised our dinner and we had a glass of wine and we were chatting away. Hazel said to me, 'I was trying to remember when I first met you.' And I said, 'Well, I was too, the other day. It was at the Brotherhood of St Laurence and the connection was Concetta Benn.' Hazel said, 'Oh, Connie Benn . . .' and got a piece of paper and she started writing down 'Connie Benn'. She said, 'I have to write down everything because I forget. I write myself notes all day long.' I said, 'That's a good idea. I do, too.' She then started to write a letter to Connie: 'I'd like to see you. I haven't thought or heard of you for some time . . .' So we talked about Connie and about another mutual friend, Jan Marsh, and things like that.

At this point in the evening she was in really fine form. She did say to me that the thought of not being able to live in her own house was not good, that she'd like to think her life was over if it came to that point. She said, 'I'd really like to die in my own house.' This was not a morbid conversation; she talked about it more or less in passing. She also told me that she was still enraged she had Alzheimer's. The evening was still relatively early, although we had drunk a good couple of glasses of wine by this stage. She said, 'I know I'm better off that it's known. But I'm furious. I was just having the best life. A lot of that's gone away.' As I've said earlier, one of the most wonderful things about Hazel is that she never gave up on growing as a person. And that, of course, is the incredible sadness of her lot now. And she can articulate that. Her life has been one of constant growth – intellectual growth, social growth and achievement. Now, she says, 'I'm bloody 74 and I've been dealt this bum steer. I'm not growing. I'm being diminished. And it's not what I chose.'

We talked a bit about what else she might like to do

in the short-term that we could do together. Hazel said, 'Music's the best thing for me. I just can respond and it's there and it's overwhelming and I love it.' She also said she'd like to try going out to the movies, so we talked about that and she said, 'Okay, but you know you'll have to organise it all because I can't remember.' I said, 'I know that. Prue and Sue will help.' And she talked a lot about Sue and Ros and how good they were to her and how important it was for her to have that family and then she said, 'What'll I do when I can't remember them?' I said, 'Well, the good thing about that is you won't know. It'll be over. But you've got a fantastic family who look after you. So you'll never know when you stop remembering.' 'Yes. I s'pose so.'

We'd eaten dinner and about an hour and a half had passed. A little earlier I'd thought I should go, but Hazel said, 'Oh, don't go yet, it's so nice to have you here.' And so I stayed. We were still chatting away and Hazel said, 'How's that friend of yours, Quentin?' Quentin Bryce and I are very close, but Quentin is also a good friend of Hazel's. I said, 'She's going well.' 'Where'd she go?' 'She went to live in Queensland.' 'Has she got any children?' 'Yes. Quite a lot.' 'She's got a nice husband, hasn't she?' 'Yes.' 'Yes, he's like your Gordon. I think he's a really good man. You're lucky to have married good men.' And then all of a sudden in the middle of the conversation she turned around and looked at me in total surprise. I was wondering if I could have said something that had offended her, although I couldn't think what. She said, 'Who are you?' I said, 'I'm Wendy.' She said, 'Are you sure you're Wendy?' I said, 'Yes.' It was so strange that at first I thought it was bit of a game. But it wasn't. It was quite real. She was looking at me as if I'd just dropped into the room from another planet and she could not understand how I'd got there.

I tried to stay calm on the surface but underneath I felt really panicky. I didn't know where all this was going to go. I almost felt she was going to be angry. She said, 'You don't look like Wendy.' I said, 'That's because when you first knew me I had dark hair. I'm a blonde now. I'm a grey-blonde.' 'I'm not sure if you are Wendy. Could you be someone else?' 'No. I'm definitely Wendy.' 'Well how will I know?' 'I don't know. You'll just have to believe me. But I am Wendy.' It was unnerving. And it went on for probably five or six minutes, which is quite a long time in a conversation between two people.

I said, 'Perhaps if we talked about some of the things we did together you'd remember.' Hazel said, 'That's a good idea.' So we talked about a couple of things and then she kind of 'clicked back in' and she banged her hand on the table and said, 'I just can't bear it, Wendy. I'm not burning the house down. I can cook my dinner. I can't drive the car. My memory just keeps going. I can't bear it.' Then she started writing down 'Wendy' and she said,

'Who's your husband?' I said, 'Gordon.' 'That's right. And you've got a Sophie, haven't you?' 'Yes.' 'And some boys . . .' 'Yes.' 'Well, I'll write their names down. If I write them down I might remember them then. Now where's your farm?' I told her. 'Yes.' Then she asked again. She must have asked me 20 times where the farm was.

Looking back, I definitely stayed too long. I was there about two and a half hours. The first hour and a half was perfect but after that I think the strain began to tell on Hazel. It's the strain of just interacting. It's not about keeping up with the verbal flow because when she's 'there' she's as verbally agile as ever. I think it's just the strain of another person. As well, we drank a bottle of wine between us, and I think she may have had some before I arrived. That would have been fine previously, but now I think more than one drink is probably not a good idea. So next time I'll make the visit shorter and probably earlier in the day, and we'll have tea rather than wine.

That roller-coaster of a night was the strongest demonstration that I've had of the slippage. I had some really sad moments, and I found myself quite distressed when I left. The other thing that was sad was admitting to myself that Hazel looks different now. I'd been travelling a lot on business and this was the first time I'd seen her in two months or more. A couple of people had seen Hazel out at things and commented to me that they thought she looked different. I said, 'No, no, no.'

But I had to admit to myself that she does have a slightly different look. It's not just physical, it's somehow that there's a part of her missing. I found that really quite heart-breaking. And it's hard to talk about all this because I want to be honest but if Hazel reads this book I don't want it to make her feel sad about it. I've been thinking about it all a lot. Before I went to visit Hazel I'd read an astonishing book by Sue Miller called *The Story of My Father*, about his Alzheimer's and how she cared for him. It's given me a lot of insight into the disease. I suppose for me the optimism coming out of the sad moments with Hazel is the possibility that knowing more about it can help people understand more.

Sue Miller writes about the way she would identify her own memory loss with her father's and how she realised in retrospect she probably shouldn't have done. I found myself doing that with Hazel. I'd never noticed before that I was doing it. Then I thought about it and realised I should be acknowledging the grief of memory loss and not trying to pretend that it wasn't as real as it is by saying, 'I've got that, too.' I could see that it was really important to Hazel for me to understand the rage that was still there, and the worry of it. The worry of 'Where does it go from here?'

Hazel's legacy is a very powerful one – the energy and leadership she showed in community causes. How could that little girl on the outskirts of Perth, riding a bicycle in the sandhills, have imagined the life she's led. How could she imagine that she would be adored by this nation, that she'd be able to provide leadership in so many parts of Australian life? She's been a wonderful role model. And she continues to be. Through her I hope that more people, like me, get an understanding of what Alzheimer's is, are able to recognise the disease and its impact, and are aware but not frightened of it. We need to know a huge amount more to help us understand it, and we also need to work out how we are going to manage it as a nation. If the leadership Hazel is showing now in her own experience with the disease helps in that, it will be another wonderful legacy.

CHAPTER 16

# The Road Ahead

HOW WILL THE REST of our journey unfold? It is, of course, impossible to know. Real-life stories can only be told looking back. Obviously this one offers no hope of rescue or a happy ending; we know that the trend for someone suffering from Alzheimer's disease is one of inexorable decline. But real life is organic – chaotic and unpredictable. Life as you actually live it cannot be reduced to a line on a graph. So although we know what the general direction will be, that doesn't make us any the wiser about the detail or nuance of what lies ahead for Mum.

Professor Brodaty says that the overall course of the disease is often characterised by a very slow rate of decline, sometimes it even plateaus; then the decline becomes more rapid, as though it's turned a corner. He explains the progress of the disease by comparing it to the way little children develop: there is a point where they are suddenly walking – there's a threshold of enough brain-power to do it – then there's a plateau, then they're suddenly talking – another threshold has been reached. For people whose brains are being eroded by Alzheimer's, it's the reverse: they lose a critical threshold of neurones and with it the ability to carry out certain functions. But which parts of the brain are affected, at what rate particular capacities are lost, and how these affect someone's life, vary from person to person.

Thinking about the future leads me to wondering about our attitudes generally towards ageing. It seems to me that our modern preoccupation with remaining youthful, combined with our failure to sufficiently value 'our elders' as a font of wisdom and experience, leaves us personally and socially impoverished. Add to this our fear and avoidance of death in general, and our own death in particular, and it doesn't bode well for our experience of our later years. Characterised all too often by frailty and irrelevance, they can seem to be merely an addendum to the more vivid, 'real' part of our lives.

Add the bogy of dementia to our underlying phobia of ageing, and we have a potent mix indeed. In her story on dementia in *The Bulletin*, 'Thanks for the memories', Diana Bagnall wrote:

> Growing old is bad enough, but growing old and senile terrifies us . . . In a secular society which places rational thought on a pedestal, dementia challenges our core

notion of what it is to be human. I think (reasonably), therefore I am. So who, and what, am I when thought becomes laboured, when learning is undone and when the thread of language, which connects me to others around me begins to fray and break? Am I still worth knowing?

These reflections are in the back of my mind as I consider Mum's particular experience of ageing with Alzheimer's. I have written about our sadness that the disease has deprived her of the older age she might otherwise have had. Mum has fought in her own way against the very idea that people should be limited in their opportunities by notions and structural constraints attached to labels. The idea that life is less fully available to be lived, by virtue of being a woman, or black, or poor, or old, was anathema to her. Just as she stood against those limitations as an issue of social justice, she struggled against them personally.

By the time she had separated from Dad, and settled in her 'new' life, she had slain many of the demons that might have restrained her. She had the confidence and determination to 're-invent' her life yet again, and looked forward to a vibrant older age. She was pragmatic and unsqueamish about the physical infirmities that she supposed might come her way sooner or later, and about her eventual death. The one thing she was *not* prepared for was the erosion of her mind, her very sense of who she is; the loss of the capacity to determine, for herself, the course of the rest of her life.

And thus her anger. She has struggled, with some success, to accept the hand dealt her, but at times cannot escape a sense of rage at this particular fate, or her feelings of powerlessness in the face of it. She knows it is futile, but it nevertheless surfaces at times (especially if she has had more than a glass of wine!). The pain caused by this self-awareness, albeit diminished, is heartbreaking to be with. And therein lies the knife-edge of mixed feelings, which I'm sure is shared by others who have loved ones with dementia. As you are mourning the losses, you are grateful for the mercy that comes with them. You hope the fog will be gentle as it descends further, until there is no pain.

Dealing with Alzheimer's and its effects certainly brings up questions about who a person is, who any of us are, beneath or beyond the external expression and internal coherence that rely on a functional brain. Are we merely the sum total of our memories, feelings, thoughts, and other cognitive processes? Do *we* disappear as they recede? Do we become a physical shell, with anything of our 'true selves' existing more in the memories of others than in anything we now are? Or is there an indestructible core, an essence that exists for (at least) as long as we are alive?

There are many possible answers to these deeply personal questions: some would suggest there is no core beneath cognition or emotion; others say we are, at root, a soul or buddha nature, a 'lifeforce' that is intact throughout this life, and maybe beyond. I am not trying to suggest there's any right answer, merely to say that this journey has certainly made me ponder these questions even more than before. And I've found that exploring my own deep beliefs has helped me to 'be' with Mum even as her 'outer being' slowly disintegrates.

I understand, from being with Mum, and talking to people who work in the field, for people with Alzheimer's life is increasingly experienced through the emotions. It becomes more of a 'feeling' life, and this outlives the capacity to articulate experience. An obvious consequence of this seems to me to be that we owe people with Alzheimer's the respect and effort of being attuned and responsive to their emotions and sensitivities, especially as these become, perhaps, less nuanced or obvious to us.

I am reminded of something Lewis Kaplan has said to me on more than one occasion. Although deeply compassionate he is not, in my experience, given to offering platitudinous comforts. But he tells me that when he talks to people who've lived through the end stages and death of loved ones with Alzheimer's they often say that in the end, when all else is stripped away, what is left is a simple, strong, pure love. Whatever the future holds for Mum, and however difficult it may at times be, I hope with all my heart that this is true for her, and for us.

~

IN WHAT I AM thinking of as the 'middle period' of this journey, life is not bad at all. We've moved through the early stages of uncertainty, diagnosis, fear, and a time dominated by the anger.

Life now is more settled, gentler, funnier and accepting. Mum's anger is less frequent, and does not last long. She is very loving. Life has become more of a moment-to-moment experience. And most of these moments are happy.

Recently I have seen a 'closing in' happening with Mum. It seems reasonable to expect that we'll be seeing more and more of this contraction. Both Prue and Gail have noticed that lately when they've asked her if she'd like to go with them to do this or that she'll often now say, 'Oh no, I'm all right,' whereas not so long ago she would often have said yes. Part of it seems to be less initiative, less get up and go, but partly it seems also to be a reserved contentment with just being in her house or pottering around the garden.

The other thing I'm seeing increasingly is that she can be more absent or remote, which is not at all how she was before the disease. She has tended to be very 'present' when she's with someone. But increasingly, she'll 'zone out'. She comes back to the moment, but I expect the absences, the distance, will increase as the Alzheimer's progresses.

She can catch me unawares, though, with the layers of understanding and memory she still has. Prue told me that when they had been talking recently Mum had mentioned that Jan and Ben are currently in France. This surprised me, because she'd seemed very foggy about it, which I'd thought seemed perfectly understandable, given that she is so used to them being around. But she said to Prue that although she knew where they were, she didn't like to ask me how they were going, 'because I think it's a bit tender for Sue'. Sophie later told me Mum had said something similar to her, too.

I was moved, and it showed me something valuable about how Mum is still able to absorb information about things within her inner orbit of concerns. After we moved in, it took about two weeks for her to become clear that we were finally living next door, but now it's an established fact for her. In the same way, she has been able to establish and retain the fact that two members of the family are in France. Her hesitance in bringing that up with me also shows that her empathy is functioning strongly. Mum is so caring about other people generally and her family in particular that she is still able to think empathically, which can be difficult because of the layers of information processing and nuanced thinking it requires. It reinforces my inner sense that while Mum's short-term memory is shot and her cognitive processes are increasingly confused, there are core things about her that are still intact.

In practical terms I know that the problem solving, which is an inherent part of providing support and care to someone with Alzheimer's, will be ongoing. The disease doesn't stop in its tracks, which means that there's always a new challenge or limitation to be dealt with. I don't want to rely too much on the reverse metaphor of children growing to describe what happens as dementia takes hold, but there is no doubting the strong parallels. When you have little children you get your house crawl-proof, then one day they're hauling themselves up to standing and everything they might pull down on top of themselves has to be shifted further up. Then they are able to climb and the process has to be repeated. You constantly need to adapt to changing capacity, as you do for someone with Alzheimer's. These things can be small, such as having to find Mum the same kind of cord on which to keep her front door key after she lost the last one, because she can't easily recognise the key on a different kind of holder. Or they can be bigger, such as knowing that we can't let her wander off alone now even in familiar environments away from home. It's a dance, and you have to take your lead from where the person is at the time, cognitively and emotionally.

As Mum's condition worsens she will inevitably, gradually, need more care. Now that my family is living next door to her, we have bought some extra time before we need to implement significant change. But this is unlikely to last indefinitely. For all the public affection out there for her, Mum is in the same position as anyone else – ultimately there are only a few people who will be there for her.

And, like most people in this situation, we feel committed to doing everything we can to see that Mum gets that care in her own home – the home she loves so much – rather than in a nursing home. But pulling that off is going to involve some creativity. We don't have the means to pay for full-time care. So we're thinking laterally to see what other options there are. One that we're considering is converting her garage into a small bed-sit and having someone we trust live in there and be a back-up for whatever will need doing, or in case of an emergency. We have already discussed this with Mum, presenting it to her as a way of her helping out someone who needs a place to live. It's stretching the truth, but it means she retains her feelings of dignity and control over her own space. Whatever needs to be done we don't want it to be painful or upsetting if we can help it.

But even if we are able to work out something like this, I know that I need to contemplate the nursing home options in case they are needed in the future. I deeply, sincerely hope that never happens, but I know it would be irresponsible not to do some investigating soon so that we are prepared. My reluctance to face this option is reinforced by Mum's previous vehemence that she would rather die than move to a home. But I'm sure that most of the people who are in nursing homes have families who vowed they would never resort to nursing-home care. However unwillingly, they have had to take that option, and if I am honest, so might we. If it gets to the point where Mum needs 24-hour care it would be naive to think we could personally provide it, or that she would even want us to. I certainly couldn't fulfil her needs and also work to support my family, which I have to do.

I *know* this with the rational part of my brain, but right now, mid-2004, it's in the 'too hard' basket. I recognise what's happening here – it's what I think of as 'sniffing the beast'. With something like this, which is painful and unsettling to contemplate, I find that I prefer to let myself approach the thought slowly, then back off, then get a bit closer next time.

While there is no urgency, I can gradually reconcile logic and emotion – head and heart. Eventually, I'll 'embrace the beast', which in this case means taking practical steps to put Mum's name on the waiting list of one or more suitable nursing homes in case we ever need to go to that. At the moment the thought of even compiling a list is too demoralising (Prue has done some preliminary research but I'm not even interested in opening her file on it yet). But making a list and checking them out is something I'll have to do before too much longer. The fact that I currently regard Mum moving into a nursing home as an option to be avoided does not mean that I won't do all I can to get the very best one for her needs, if it comes to that.

I also hope that the thickening fog of Alzheimer's means that if it does come to it then Mum may not object to it in the strenuous way she has in the past. It's hard to know, because when it recently came up in a low-key way, Mum was quite surprisingly pragmatic and unemotional about it. But how she would feel at the time remains to be seen – whether she would be aware of what was happening is unknown. My wish is that we are able to keep Mum at home until she dies, or until she's past a point where it matters to her. My biggest fear is that there will come a point where she does need the kind of care she can only get in a nursing home and yet she is still aware enough to know and resent what is happening. That possibility is one I find heart-rending. If things do reach the point where we have to make a decision like that about her care it'll be distressing enough for the rest of us, I can only hope it isn't distressing for her.

~

WHATEVER TWISTS AND TURNS lie ahead, this particular journey is going to finish in death. I find Buddhist teachings and practices very helpful here. They suggest to me that the extent to which we can fully embrace life is influenced by the degree to which we can embrace the reality of death. For me this has layers of meaning and truth that deepen as I explore and face them.

With Alzheimer's you are slowly losing the person you knew and relied on. The grieving for that sets in early, and waves of it can come with every fresh milestone of loss. But I've found that if you can also see and feel what you're *not* losing it helps you find a way through. Instead of relating to the person as someone who can't do this or that, you can relate to them as somebody who *is* this and that, and who you love and respect and value for those qualities. This sense of love and value persists, even if you need sometimes to reinforce it with your memory of who they 'were'. I've found this awareness helps me get over the periodic humps of frustration and sadness that come with the disease.

I suppose the idea is that by not getting too caught up in our own aversion and sorrow, by getting our attention off the negative, by seeking to accept what is happening, not with resignation or passivity, but with whatever grace and gentle realism we can muster, we reduce our own suffering and become more useful to others. Whereas fear and struggle have the opposite effect: they exacerbate suffering and self-concern. This kind of calmness and acceptance takes work and time for most of us. The practice of meditation is a way in for many people, and there's a good reason it's called practice. I've been studying and practising meditation intermittently for more than two decades, through yoga, qigong and Buddhism, but there is no way in the world I'd suggest I am at all accomplished. But it helps, it really helps. I also wouldn't suggest for a minute that Buddhism is the only philosophy or activity that can offer this kind of help. The equanimity fostered by the power of prayer, or faith, or simple 'being', no matter what form it takes, is something to be valued. And though Mum no longer adheres to any organised religion, I know it has comforted her to know that people include her in their thoughts or their prayers – as people of many different faiths, and none, have written to tell us they do.

It is also comforting for me to think about what a difference Mum has made; how well she has lived; how she has been committed to doing her bit to make the world a better place, and how she has succeeded in this in so many different ways. There's a quote that pops up regularly, something ABC-TV's Quentin Dempster said at the time of Mum's pituitary surgery. He said, 'The nearest thing we have to a saint is probably Hazel Hawke.' I have to laugh – Mum is no saint, as she'd be the first to tell you: 'Oh, Barleys!!' But she has established herself in people's hearts and minds as a damn good person. That was the case long before she was ever a public figure. I know it myself, and many other people have told me it over the years. She has simply been someone good to have in your life, who made a contribution and was strongly connected to her friends, her community, her family; someone who cared, someone who did her best. To have her as a mother is an absolute blessing.

Her life unfolded in such a way that she got to take those qualities onto the national stage. There was no contrivance from her about what she chose to do in that role. And it was clear to people that it wasn't an act. You saw that if you were out and about with her. The way she responded to people, the way she would really connect with them, and truly want to hear their stories. You can't fake that one on one. People related to the fact that she wasn't up herself or arrogant and yet she did find a confidence and a willingness to speak her mind. All those qualities of hers endeared her to Australia in the same way they endeared her to us closest to her.

And now she's summoned her courage and shared the very thing she fears being demeaned by, in a plea to us all to do what we can to ensure that others suffer less from fear, stigma and isolation now and into the future. In seeing Mum with Alzheimer's disease, people can see a woman who is somehow altered and yet in other ways still herself, who is bringing her characteristic humility and determination to the closing episode of an eventful life. Maybe we all hope that if it were us that is how we could be, too.

# Information and Help

# News from the Front

My experiences with Mum have taught me a lot about Alzheimer's disease first-hand, and I've also sought out information in the past few years. But still, it's only one person's experience. Mum's particular journey with Alzheimer's has been, and will continue to be, similar to many people's, but also particular to her.

There are many, many people out there doing wonderful work on the front-line of this disease – doctors, researchers, counsellors, advocates – as well as people with Alzheimer's themselves, and the people in their lives. In order to get the latest information, and gain a broader perspective, I spoke to some of these people. All were generous with their time and their valuable insights.

You've already met **Lewis Kaplan**, the chief executive of the NSW branch of Alzheimer's Australia, in the pages of this book; **Henry Brodaty**, AO, is the chairman of Alzheimer's Disease International and Professor of Old Age Psychiatry at Sydney's Prince of Wales Hospital; **Fay Crampton** is a Dementia Support Consultant at Alzheimer's Australia; **Mary Roddy** is co-ordinator of the Living with Memory Loss program run by Alzheimer's Australia; and **Marilyn MacArthur** is a group leader for the program. (**Dr Richard Schloeffel** is a holistic medical practitioner and Mum's GP. His comments appear at the end of this section.)

**Sue Pieters-Hawke**: *How many people in Australia have Alzheimer's disease? What are the odds that an individual will develop it?*

**Lewis Kaplan**: More than 170,000 Australians have a diagnosis of dementia, with perhaps as many again in the early or pre-diagnostic stages of dementia. There are 70 or 80 different diseases that cause dementia. Alzheimer's is, if you like, the IBM of dementia: up to 70% of dementias are caused by Alzheimer's.

**Professor Henry Brodaty**: It's very rare to have dementia below the age of 60. Even between 60 and 70 it's probably only 1% of the population, maybe a little bit more, who have. But then it doubles every five years. So you start with 0.7% between 60 and 64. That's not much, but then it's 1.4% between 65 and 69, 2.8% between 70 and 74, 5.6% for 75 to 79, 11.2% for 80 to 84 and

22.4% for 85 to 89. It's going up pretty steeply the longer you live, and people are living longer.

**LK**: Fifty percent of people with dementia in Australia are over the age of 85, and that age group is growing very rapidly: the Queen sent out more than 35,000 telegrams for people over 100 across the Commonwealth last year.

**SPH**: *It is a fatal disease, isn't it – in other words, for Alzheimer's there is no survival rate . . . ?*

**HB**: Yes. Although the other thing is, for instance, a patient in his mid-eighties who I saw last week, who has developed Alzheimer's disease. Now it may be that the disease outlives him. People who are 85 are going to die from something in the next few years, mostly. It's a perverse way of saying there's some good news and bad news, but it's possible that they won't die of the disease. They'll die of something else before they get that bad.

**SPH**: *What are the most common early symptoms of Alzheimer's?*

**HB**: There can be changes in personality, which are only recognised in retrospect. Memory problems. Word finding difficulties, particularly more unusual words or complex words.

So you might know it's a watch but can't think of the word 'buckle' or 'band'. We all forget words or people's names or their faces or where we parked the car. But it's the accumulation, it happening time after time, a consistent pattern emerging. It's not just when the person's tired or got the 'flu or had too much to drink. It's happening on a repeated, daily basis, and it's progressive. When that's happening then people should start worrying. We look at its progression. Is it affecting more than just a few isolated bits of memory? Is it also interpreting complex information? Is it also affecting language? Is it also affecting visio-spatial skills?

It also depends on the level at which that person's functioning. If the person doesn't use their brain all that much, if their routine is housework and doing a bit of knitting, or doing a bit of labouring work and so forth, and it doesn't make much in the way of cognitive demands, then he or she may not notice those things. Whereas I recently saw a very prominent legal specialist who's in his seventies now and says he isn't feeling as sharp as he was, and he gives me examples. If you test him he's still well above average, but he's noticing there's a difference.

**LK**: I've got a doctor friend who says, 'The people who ring me up and say, "I'm sure I've got Alzheimer's. I lost my keys last Tuesday afternoon at 2.30 pm," don't have anything to worry about. They remembered that they forgot. The ones who've really got Alzheimer's don't come and see me because they don't remember.'

**SPH**: *How is 'early diagnosis' actually defined?*

**HB**: There's no clear-cut definition in terms of it being, say, within one year or two years of symptoms appearing. It's really a diagnosis that's made when the person is still functioning and to outsiders there's no obvious impairment, but the person himself or herself or those living with the person can discern that there are some problems emerging.

**LK**: I think the thing is to define it in relation to the person still having insight and capacity. Insight into the fact that things are going wrong and capacity to do something about it. The pathway is a one-way downward slope and eventually people will lose the insight that there's anything wrong and they will start living more in the moment. But also people lose the capacity to make levels of decisions. If I had early stage Alzheimer's and I went to the supermarket to buy a box of cereal I might still have the idea that if I give you a $20 note you'll give me some change and I'll put it in my pocket and that's a fair transaction. But I might no longer have the skill to be able to make complex decisions about stockmarket transactions. I might not be able to work out my share if six of us have gone for lunch and the bill is $373. But perhaps I can still do a 50–50 split if there's just the two of us. So gradually capacity reduces, and the key question about capacity becomes legal capacity: Do I have the legal capacity to make binding decisions? And who should measure or decide this?

**SPH**: *Early diagnosis is something I've given a lot of thought to. A lot of people resist diagnosis, as indeed we did for quite a while. What are your thoughts on the pros and cons of early diagnosis?*

**LK**: Well, often the people themselves do want to know. A very common comment we hear is 'I've been feeling like I'm going mad. It's really a relief to know that I'm not going mad, that there's an explanation. It's an organic disease. It's not my fault.' Which is not to deny that the moment when you are told, 'You've got Alzheimer's' is a world-shattering moment. It's extremely confronting, even if you know there's something wrong. And let's face it, most people seem to know for a year or two or three that all is not well before they actually get to a point of looking into it. Often it's the partner who says, 'Look, things aren't right. You aren't the same person you used to be. Let's go and find out what's wrong.' And if you leave it too long the person will be so confused they may no longer realise there is a problem.

Another big argument for early diagnosis is the chance to put your affairs in order while you still have capacity to do so – I think the number of people who don't have a will is still around 30%. What you ideally need with early dementia is to get an Enduring Power of Attorney and an Enduring Guardianship order, because you know there's a very likely chance of you still being alive but not being able to make decisions on your own behalf. And later on if there's conflict, for instance two adult children who both believe that they're doing the right thing by you but one wants to do X and the other wants to do Y, if you don't have capacity you may end up at the Guardianship Tribunal.

**HB**: Diagnosis also allows for assistance from medication and for the person and those around them to develop effective coping strategies. Every week I'm giving somebody a diagnosis and I'll say, 'Your life is not going to change from today to tomorrow. In fact you're going to have exactly the same sort of life and, with medication, even maybe a slightly improved one. It's a very long process, a slow process. There'll be some things that you won't be able to do and you'll develop mechanisms or strategies to cope with those. If you have a bad leg, you use a crutch; if you've got a bad memory you work out strategies to cope with your poor memory. But having Alzheimer's doesn't mean you can't enjoy life.'

**Fay Crampton**: I don't think ignorance is bliss. In the beginning there is denial, which is normal, and shock. But I think it's important to know what's ahead and to make decisions about what you want. Things change as the disease progresses, and sometimes very quickly. And lots of decisions have to be made very quickly. So if you've at least had a look at it, and thought about it and talked about it with your family, then it makes it a little bit easier, I think.

**Mary Roddy**: Early diagnosis also allows for a good differential diagnosis to be made. Not every person who shows signs of dementia can be assumed to have dementia. Other conditions can cause symptoms that mimic dementia: for example, depression, thyroid problems, severe infection, or Vitamin B12 deficiency. A person who is not taking their medications correctly may develop dementia-like symptoms. In these cases, if the condition is treated or corrected, the symptoms disappear.

Early diagnosis also allows the person and family to plan for the future, to develop appropriate support networks and to find as much information as possible to help them travel the long pathway of the dementia. Without an early diagnosis, the person concerned, and their family, forgo the opportunity to gain valuable information and support that will facilitate acceptance and enable them to make more informed choices and decisions. Without early diagnosis, as the dementia progresses, the family faces enormous frustrations because of the constant changes associated with dementia. Families are not equipped to deal with these frustrations unaided. Also, the person with dementia may eventually endanger themselves or others.

**SPH**: *And what about the negatives of early diagnosis?*

**Marilyn MacArthur**: Unfortunately there is a stigma attached to a diagnosis of dementia in the community. Ongoing education is required within the community and among health professionals, to bring about increased acceptance and understanding. Early diagnosis may expose people to negative attitudes and some people choose not to seek diagnosis until symptoms become more obvious. The impact on people still in the work force may involve modifying their workload or giving up work. Employers and colleagues can often trigger an early diagnosis after observing a pattern of deterioration in performance over time. Despite the crisis this causes in people's lives, sometimes it can come as a great relief to be freed from the effort of covering up constantly.

**MR**: To me, one of the most important things we should address about diagnosis, whether it's early or late, is something I've heard doctors and other professionals say, which is, 'Well, there's nothing we can do for them so what's the point in telling them?' I would never subscribe to that view. There is so much that people in early dementia, and their families, can do for themselves.

**MM**: I think that giving people a diagnosis actually helps them to understand themselves and what's happening to them.

**MR**: And it helps the people who are caring for them too. Knowing someone has a certain condition that's affecting them physically or mentally or emotionally will help others to know how to be with them. Carers can have a much richer and more genuine relationship with the person they are supporting if they have access to appropriate information.

**SPH**: *You've spoken about the relief some people feel when they receive their diagnosis, but others genuinely don't want to know, do they?*

**HB**: It's an issue that always comes up. The family say, 'Should we tell them the diagnosis or not?' There was a survey done overseas a few years ago in which people were asked, 'If you had Alzheimer's, would you want to be told?' And the vast majority said yes. Next question was, 'If your spouse had Alzheimer's, should they be told?' and an equally vast majority said no. So it was a double standard. What I teach doctors and students is, people have a right to know their diagnosis and people have a right not to know their diagnosis, and our job as clinicians, and our skill, is to determine which it is.

If I was giving a diagnosis to you I'd say, 'You've got a problem with your memory and that shows up in your tests, and it's a degenerative problem that commonly occurs as people grow older. Are there any other questions you want to ask me about that?' And during this I'm monitoring your response. 'This can be caused by a disease. Would you like me to discuss it?' So I'm giving it step by step and then looking for the response. And if people are getting anxious or people are giving me clear signals either overtly or covertly they don't want to hear any more, I stop.

I always tell the family. I never withhold that diagnosis from the family. Probably I withhold the diagnosis from the patient maybe about 20% to 30% of the time, somewhere around there. Most people want to know. What they do with that then: some people will forget, some people will put it out of their minds and not because they've forgotten it but because they're using denial as a way of coping with it. And that's fine, too. Some people get really upset by it.

If the person has heard it and processed it then I start doing the other things, saying, 'Your life is not going to change from one day to the next. There are treatments that can stop you getting worse symptomatically. There's no cure, it's not going to stop the underlying disease process' – I'm very straight about that – 'but other treatments are being developed which may be a cure and they're on the horizon, and hopefully in time for you.' So I give them that hope that something will develop as well.

**SPH**: *Can you explain what those treatments that are available now are and how they work?*

**HB**: The way the drugs work is they boost one of the chemicals in your brain that's particularly important for memory, that's acetylcholine. It happens to be the most important chemical for memory and also the chemical that's most affected in Alzheimer's. So blocking the enzyme that destroys acetylcholine boosts levels of it and people maintain their cognitive abilities for longer. There's also some functional improvement.

Things like managing your medication, operating a telephone, operating your video machine, driving the car, managing public transport. Those things also seem to be maintained longer for people on drugs versus placebo.

The three drugs are donepezil (marketed as Aricept and distributed by Pfizer), galantamine (Reminyl made by Janssen) and rivastigmine (Exelon made by Novartis). So, there are three different drug companies. There are perhaps some slight differences in side effects, but there are no convincing data to show one is better than the other. Studies promoted by Pfizer show their drug is better than the one by Janssen. Studies promoted by Janssen show the reverse, and so on. But they're not double-blind studies, they're open-label [in other words the researchers know which drug they are trialling during the experiments]. For practical purposes the drugs are all doing the same thing.

Last year a drug called memantine (marketed as Ebixa, made by Lundbeck) came out, and it works in a different way altogether. It's an NNDA-receptor antagonist. It stops excito-toxins causing brain death or dysfunctional brain cells. What happens with Alzheimer's is there's more glutamate, which is a chemical in the brain which causes calcium to flow into brain cells, and that's exciting to the brain cells and it's also toxic, so that's why they call it excito-toxin. You can partially plug the holes that let in the calcium with this memantine. It can be used in conjunction with the cholinesterase inhibitors [the drugs previously described]; it works in a different way.

The outcome is modest. It's of some benefit. It's been mainly trialled in people with moderate to severe Alzheimer's whereas the first three drugs I was talking about are for mild to moderate. It's approved in Australia for moderate to severe Alzheimer's, although it's not subsidised by the PBS here. But many of my patients are taking both. Even though they have mild disease, they're taking both.

**SPH**: *How long in the progression of the disease do these drugs keep working for?*

**HB**: We don't know because until very recently no trial had gone beyond 12 months. The gold standard [in scientific research] is a placebo-controlled trial, but it's not ethical to keep people on placebo for long periods of time, and nowadays when we've got proven treatments with modest efficacy there are strong arguments that it's unethical to do any placebo-controlled trials.

Having said that, a study was published in *The Lancet* in July [2004] of a trial which ran for two years. It found positive effects, although less than previously reported. But there were methodological concerns about the study.

What we do know is that people who are on the drug will have a slight improvement or a maintenance of cognitive function for a period of time. Not everyone. Some people will continue to decline despite the drug. Whether they are declining at a slower rate than they would have without the drug you can't tell.

What I tell people as a rough rule of thumb is that about a third of people will show some improvement for a period of time, a third of people will stay the same, and a third of people will continue to decline. Whether they're declining slower than they would have without the drug, I can't tell. And I can't predict which third you will be in. Eventually, everybody declines.

On the average, if you look at cognition over time in placebo-versus-drug treatment, the drug treatment is about a year ahead of the placebo. So you'll see a modest improvement on the average, and then a gradual decline and then they're back to where they started about nine to 12 months later, whereas the people on placebo are still going downhill. Now that doesn't mean you stop at 12 months, because if you stay on it you stay a year ahead of where you would've been otherwise.

There is some debate in scientific circles about whether the slope of decline differs, about whether in fact the rate of decline is slower in people on drugs than not. But if I had Alzheimer's I would take the drug. No question of it.

**SPH**: *What about the vitamins and non-prescription supplements we hear a lot about?*

**HB**: People take vitamin E, they'll take vitamin C, they'll take folic acid, they'll take Gingko biloba. I recommend vitamins

E and C because there is some evidence that they may be helpful. It's pretty slim, but they seem harmless and they're not that expensive. Folic acid if the people have a high homocysteine level. It's an amino acid or protein in the blood, and high levels have been linked to heart problems and also Alzheimer's and stroke, and you can lower that very easily with folic acid, which is what women take during pregnancy and it's harmless and very cheap, so I recommend that. (I take vitamin E and vitamin C and folic acid. If you go to a meeting of neurologists in the United States and ask who is taking vitamin E, half the audience will put up their hand. So doctors are very aware of it.)

With Gingko biloba, again the evidence is very slim but there is some that it may be of some benefit. It has a number of properties: it's an antioxidant; it inhibits platelet aggregation, which is what aspirin does – it makes blood flow smoother so it's less likely to form clots; and it has mild anti-inflammatory action as well. So it's got a lot of things going for it. In many countries it's very popular, like Germany where it's the top-selling drug. A lot of people swear by it. There've been probably 50 trials of some sort in dementia with Gingko. Only a couple of them have been very rigorous trials. One of them showed a benefit, one of them hasn't. It doesn't seem to be a risky drug although it is a blood thinner and can cause bleeding, so you might have to be a bit cautious with it.

**SPH**: *Do we know what causes Alzheimer's?*

**HB**: There are things that have been shown to be risk factors and things that have been shown to be protective factors. The risk factors are: having head injury with loss of consciousness; things that are bad for your heart – high blood pressure, high cholesterol, smoking – at first, studies showed that smoking may be a protective factor, but that was knocked down and subsequent studies have shown it may be a risk factor.

In the '70s and '80s there was a lot of circumstantial evidence that pointed to aluminium, but that seems to have died off. What was found is there is aluminium in the plaque in the brains of people with Alzheimer's when you stain the plaque and look at it under the microscope. What wasn't realised was that the stain had the aluminium in it, and when the researchers re-did the analyses with a huge atomic microscope that could identify the plaque without the stain they didn't find higher rates of aluminium in the brains of those with Alzheimer's. You probably shouldn't use aluminium cookingware with acidic foods like rhubarb or tomato or something like that, because you can leach the aluminium out. But aluminium is one of the most abundant elements on earth. You can never have aluminium deficiency; you're always constantly exposed to it.

Protective factors are: more education; maybe a diet rich in antioxidants like vitamin E; maybe supplements of vitamin E and vitamin C; maybe eating more fish, maybe taking a statin – a cholesterol-lowering drug; maybe being on long-term non-steroidal anti-inflammatories, like for rheumatoid arthritis – people on those appear to have a lower rate of Alzheimer's disease. And up until last year it was thought that maybe for women post-menopausally taking hormone replacement therapy was a protective factor, but then the reverse findings came out in a double-blind control trial. Alcohol in moderation may be a protective factor. People like hearing that.

**SPH**: *Like a lot of people who have a parent with Alzheimer's I have worried at times about developing it myself. If I lose something I might say, 'Is this early onset?', and I'm mostly joking, but not totally. There is a concern there. What does the research so far suggest on the hereditary or genetic factors?*

**LK**: It's a very common question; people ask it all the time. The answer's quite simple. The major risk factor for developing Alzheimer's is old age. There is a small group of people, about 5% of those with Alzheimer's, who have a specific genetic variation of the disease. They often get their Alzheimer's in their late thirties to early fities. Their children have a 50% chance of having that gene. But for most people it's not a major issue.

**HB**: Your chance of having Alzheimer's now is almost nil. For a person who is the child of someone with Alzheimer's – and we're talking about Alzheimer's rather than dementia generically – their risk is double that of the general population. So at age 60 to 64 it's only a jump from 0.7% to 1.4%. Even before 70 or 75 the risk is still pretty low. Those people who have two parents with the disease must have increased odds, but we don't know the figures.

**SPH**: *Could Mum's history of physical trauma (from the tumour and surgery) plus stress have hastened the progress of incipient Alzheimer's?*

**HB**: No. There is a group of epidemiologists called the Eurodem Group who met in 1991 and pooled all their data from all around the world and they asked those sorts of questions: Can stress bring on Alzheimer's disease? And they came up with an answer: no. Can depression increase the risk of Alzheimer's? They came up with an answer: maybe. Although it's still contentious. General anaesthetics? No. But let me qualify that, because maybe if you have got early Alzheimer's and you have a general anaesthetic it can unmask it, because it makes you a bit confused anyway and if you haven't got much in the way of brain reserve then you're using all your neurons to function. As an example: if I get the 'flu nowadays I can come to work, I can function. I may be only working at 50% or 60% capacity but that's okay. But if I'm using every single nerve cell to keep me going and I drop to

50% or 60% of that, then I've come down a very steep slope. And people will notice and I will notice I'm not functioning too well. It may be the same with general anaesthetic; it may be the same with depression. It may unmask something that's happening.

**SPH**: *How much progress has been made on finding a cure for Alzheimer's?*

**HB**: In 2000 we had the prospect of a vaccine for Alzheimer's which fully stopped the disease in its tracks. It looked great. It certainly worked in mice and it looked like it was working in healthy human volunteers. But then in 2002 they pulled the plug on the trials because not only did it stimulate the body to make antibodies to the plaques and tangles – the abnormal protein in the brain with Alzheimer's – in about 17 cases out of 300 it was stimulating the body to make antibodies to the brain itself. Those people developed encephalitis and some of them died.

The researchers examined the brain of one woman who died, and it didn't have the plaques. So the vaccine had worked in terms of Alzheimer's but unfortunately it had stimulated the immune system to attack the very brain itself, not just the unhealthy bits. So they're fiddling with that to see if they can tweak the antibody response to make it safe and effective.

There are also other strategies being developed and it is possible that even in the next two years we could have something. So if you got early Alzheimer's then you can think, well I've got a few years left of quality of life and there's the possibility of a cure coming along in those few years.

**SPH**: *Let's hope. In the meantime there are a great many people living with Alzheimer's. What are the key messages you try to give to people with Alzheimer's and those close to them?*

**MR**: In our programs, we try to dispel the notion that diagnosis is a death sentence and that the person changes suddenly, at the point of diagnosis. In fact, people usually have many years to live and they are more than their dementia: they're whole people with families – children, grandchildren – occupations, interests, social lives, opinions, hopes and dreams, the same as anyone else. They need to stay connected with their own life circumstances and with the world at large.

**LK**: I was talking to a geriatrician the other day and he said he'd recently been called in to a nursing home and it was quite a good home and they'd tried various things to deal with this one man who was screaming and screaming. It turned out this man was simply in pain. A very low dose of morphine was all that it took to ease his pain and get him to stop screaming. That wasn't picked up earlier because the staff were thinking in terms of him purely through his dementia – it must be the dementia that's making him scream – rather than as a person.

**MM**: People come to our programs with tremendous fear, anxiety and anticipation, because they have been labelled with the 'dreaded dementia'. However, when they join the group program, they connect with other people who retain strengths, abilities and interests: for example, going to the theatre and movies, or perhaps to the University of the Third Age. Even if people are not as active, or are more advanced in the dementia, they're still whole people, not just their disease.

**LK**: The issue of capacity is an important one for the carers to understand. The day of diagnosis you haven't simply lost all your capacity to do everything, and that's a common complaint we hear from people with dementia: 'My partner is trying to take over my life and they see their role as a carer, where I see their role really still as my husband or wife, with a bit of extra care thrown in because I am starting to lose my capacity.'

That's a really delicate balancing act for the carer. To do enough to keep it all together, but not so much that the person they're caring for then feels resentful that their autonomy is being compromised. And yet there will come a point when their autonomy does need to be compromised, and that needs to be done as delicately and sensitively and tactfully as possible.

**SPH**: *As the disease progresses, carers and loved ones have to learn a whole new way of communicating with the person who has Alzheimer's, don't they?*

**FC**: Yes, you must join their world, they can't join yours. They are losing the capacity to be logical. It's too difficult for them. They're very conscious that things aren't working the way they used to. And that tugs at the heartstrings, seeing someone struggle like that – struggle over things that they could do before, or were very quick at before. And helping them becomes about trying to relieve that struggle, in a way. We can only try to imagine what it feels like inside their skin, but I think we need to do that.

**MM**: Carers in our programs often experience an 'Aha!' moment when they begin to 'tune into' the reality of the person with dementia. For example, if the person with dementia is hallucinating, it is important for the carer to validate the person's experience, rather than insist that they are being irrational and need to accept the carer's view.

**MR**: That's right. People begin to understand and to make the distinction between what the dementia is doing to the person and what the person is trying to say. The carer will often think the person is doing something on purpose or being uncooperative: 'Why can't you remember? We've had this appointment for how many days? And I told you six times before . . .' Remarks like this sap the person's confidence.

**FC**: I'm very big on reassurance – having the family, for instance, reassure the person with dementia. Saying that things are okay: 'We went to Phil's this morning, and then this afternoon we're going to go up the shops . . .' The main message is, 'You're okay, Mum (or Dad)' or 'It's okay.'

**SPH**: *What do people with Alzheimer's say themselves about the changes in communication?*

**MR**: I was listening to someone last week describe some of the changes that had been happening for him since the diagnosis. He said, 'Oh, I keep asking the same question.' And I said, 'Do you? Are you aware when it happens?' 'Yes,' he said. 'Yes. Oh, but my wife tells me I've asked the same question three minutes ago, and she keeps telling me . . .' and as he was speaking his fists were clenching and his whole body was tensing. I said, 'How do you feel when that happens?' 'Terrible, terrible!' he said, 'Awful.' Then I asked, 'What happens after that?' 'Well, I don't say anything.' 'Oh. And what about your wife?' 'Well, she doesn't say anything either. And then we don't speak for two days.' I asked him if the next time this happens, would he like to consider saying to his wife, 'Do you mind? When you talk to me like that I feel awful because I don't put it on. I really don't remember.'

In working through a situation like this, there is often a parallel process going on between the person and their carer – both are feeling frightened and angry. They may relinquish some of their fear and eventually resolve misunderstandings, if they can risk relating to each other more simply and honestly.

**MM**: People with dementia need to be communicated with in a way that promotes self-esteem and productivity. Some people tell us they feel they are treated 'like a child' and are not allowed to do ordinary tasks because they are not quick enough or might hurt themselves. Often, this veil of protectiveness and impatience dominates communication, so the person with dementia becomes the 'patient'. It's common for people in our groups to complain that being treated like a child prevents them using their remaining skills and abilities. On the other hand, the carers may say, 'Well look, I just don't have the time to wait for the washing up to be done' or 'The job in the garden is never finished anyway, so I might as well do it myself.' Appropriate 'duty of care' is important but overprotectiveness can rob people with dementia of feelings of dignity, productivity and self-worth. If the person feels productive and believes they are contributing to the household, what does it matter if it takes them three times as long? If it helps maintain their dignity and self-esteem, we need to tune in to their message to us that they need acceptance and 'time'.

**MR**: Marilyn's advice is crucial. Carers must be sensitive to the changes that the dementia is causing in the person. When a person has dementia, their feeling world is intact. If a carer says, 'Why can't you do it now? You did it yesterday!' or 'Look, I told you half an hour ago. Why are you asking me again?' the person with the dementia will feel demeaned. This creates anxiety which may accumulate and lead to a 'catastrophic reaction' – like a champagne cork exploding – and they may suddenly turn on the carer, or a member of the family in anger and frustration. This 'out of character' behaviour signals to the carer how the person is feeling and that they are losing the capacity to respond in a normal way.

**SPH**: *There are some great stories about carers being very creative in the way they have sort of stepped into the reality of the person with dementia, aren't there?*

**LK**: Yes, there's a lovely example in a book called *A Funny Thing Happened on the Way to the Nursing Home* by Jim Connor. His wife had dementia and he tells this wonderful story about waking up at 2.00 in the morning and his wife wasn't in bed. He got up and there she was in the formal dining room with her best clothes on and her pearls, beautifully done up, putting out the tea things, and telling him the Duchess was coming to tea. Okay, the Duchess is coming to tea, so he helped her to get the tea ready and rearranged the flowers, and everything was just absolutely spick and span for the Duchess. So they were ready and they waited. And eventually he said, 'I'll just pop out and see where she is.' And he popped out and up the road a bit, and popped back and said, 'Dear, I've just seen the Duchess's driver and he's come by to tell us the Duchess is feeling indisposed and won't be coming to tea after all. Isn't it a shame?' And they had their tea and went back to bed. That to me was a beautiful example of engaging with the person and their needs.

There's another lovely story about a woman whose husband was getting out of the house and wandering off. He wanted to go 'home' – even though he really was home. He'd get out and he'd wander off and he'd get lost, and eventually somebody would find him and bring him home, but the next time he'd wander off he'd be gone longer and longer. She was absolutely distressed and distraught. She tried dragging a heavy piece of furniture in front of the door. But he was quite big and strong and he'd drag it away and get out again. She just didn't know how to keep him in the house. So she rang up our counselling service and the counsellor talked to her and tried to find out a bit about her husband, and two pertinent facts came out. One was that he could still read, and the other was that he was an absolute gentleman. So they came up with the idea of putting a sign on the inside of the front door saying

'Ladies' Toilet'. And the gentleman never went through the door again, because it's not something he'd do.

**SPH**: *Those are lovely demonstrations of how carers can cope with altered reality, but some people go through sustained paranoia and anger and other behaviours that are even harder to cope with. Fortunately we haven't had too much of that with Mum, but I wonder what advice you give to people in that situation.*

**FC**: Sometimes when people find it very difficult to come to terms with what's happening, I have to use the words 'brain damaged', and that helps them understand that it is the damage to their brain that is causing the changed behaviour. It's not the person, it's the disease. I can think of one example of a grandfather with dementia who accused his grandson, who was about 20, of taking tools out of his garage. The grandfather moved the tools but no-one could find them and he was so angry that he was threatening his grandson. The man's wife was distressed about her grandson being accused, so my role was about normalising her husband's behaviour, helping her and her grandson understand that it was due to brain damage, and letting them both know that their experience could happen to anyone.

In that case, to deal with the situation, the grandson withdrew for a while because he needed to break the cycle. Nothing's definite with dementia. Change is happening all the time and eventually it may be that someone in that angry, paranoid state slips out of it, and it's not such a big deal. And it's often about going along with that repetitive behaviour – when he says, 'I can't find it,' say, 'Well, let's go look for it.' And actually going and looking for it. And if he wants to call the police, as another fellow did repeatedly, because he thought there had been robbers in the house, distract him into focusing on something else, like going for a coffee down the street, or for a walk. With a bit of luck, by the time you get him back, he may be focused on something else. But sometimes not – you virtually go through the same thing again. These experiences cause 'wear and tear' on carers, who have to become very aware of their own needs, especially for 'time out' from caring.

**SPH**: *What do you tell carers about avoiding that kind of 'wear and tear'?*

**HB**: Having time to themselves is very important in helping carers cope. Not becoming totally 100% immersed in the caring role, but keeping some time for the carer himself or herself. Maintaining leisure pursuits, for instance. Often carers say, 'I should give up my job,' and I say, 'Better if you don't.' Work is good for most people.

And talking about it and being open with it. For some families it's the secret: no-one must know. But when people are open about it, people can work with it. For instance someone will say, 'My husband loves golf.' But he can't play golf because he can't remember which way to hit the ball or he can't keep the score and he's breaking the rules and so the golf club won't let him play. So you go and talk to the golf club, get his buddies to go with him to play golf, and be his caddy or whatever. It works. (I'm still amazed that bowling clubs, which is a big thing for older people, have stopped people with Alzheimer's playing bowls because 'they can't play by the rules'. It's just awful.)

So, being open about it and working out strategies for dealing with things is very important. Carers looking after their own physical health is very important, too. And getting help, not being martyrs. Take things like aggression, wandering, asking the same question over and over: 'When are we going home?' 'We are home, darling,' then thirty seconds later, 'When are we going home?' You get that same question twenty times in five minutes and you get pretty irritated by it. Particularly if you haven't had much sleep because the person may sleep eight hours but it just happens to be broken up all through the 24 hours – sleep architecture is disrupted – so you're tired. You get irritated. You get snappy. Having time out is really important.

**SPH**: *It's hard to not feel weighed down by guilt when you're in a carer role to some degree or another. You can feel guilty about what* *you are doing, what you're not doing, and what you should be doing. And then when it comes to the future, even starting to think about the prospect of maybe having to take the nursing home option is almost impossible . . .*

**FC**: You often hear someone say, 'I'm never going to put my Mum in a nursing home,' and what I say to them is, 'Make decisions about what is happening at the time, and do the best you can do.'

**LK**: There comes a point for most people when a nursing home or hostel will actually be able to provide better care than you can at home. But that's a really difficult point for the carer to accept. Typically, couples will say to each other, 'Don't put me in a home, don't put me in a home.' 'I promise I won't put you in a home.' Then it comes to the point where that needs to happen. And we deal a lot in our counselling program with the guilt. With getting people to let go and helping them to realise that the quality of life is suffering for both of them because of that promise made many years ago which now doesn't have the same relevance. And by the time it comes to it, that person no longer has the capacity to say, 'I made you make that promise but I don't hold you to it anymore because I know it's too much.' People can never visualise how much care they will need.

**SPH**: *There is a lot about Alzheimer's that is sad and difficult and challenging, but there can be another side too, if you're able to get to that point . . .*

**MR**: If I think it's appropriate, I will introduce to a carer the idea that 'dementia can be a gift'. I might say to them, 'Through life, we can learn from everything that happens to us, so, can you see any gift for you in the dementia?' Rather than react negatively, they will often say they are now much more understanding and compassionate; better able to accept and love the person for whom they are caring.

**MM**: We know from the reports of families and professionals that just because the person with dementia cannot recognise loved ones that does not mean they lack an inner awareness. The journey through dementia can provide an opportunity for forgiveness and acceptance and lead to healing of relationships in the most unlikely situations.

**LK**: People talk to me about the pure love that is left. That says a lot to me . . . when all that other stuff is stripped away, all the pretensions and all the inhibitions and all the bad memories and the whatever else has gone on in our lives is stripped away, if you're lucky and there's pure love left, it's very pure.

The emotions stay intact longer than anything else. It's quite clear that the, what's the right word, 'civilised hooks' that we overlay more recently in our development and our civilisation are the first ones to go. And what gets left behind is the raw stuff. Carers talk about this, particularly former carers. Their partners have had the disease, and they've gone right through, and gone into a nursing home, and the carers have suffered the grief, and the person's died, and the carer has suffered more grief, and the thing that was left at the end was the pure love.

~

I ALSO SOUGHT the views of Dr Richard Schloeffel, who has been Mum's GP for about six years. He works at a complementary medical centre on Sydney's North Shore, and takes a holistic approach to patients, with particular attention to nutritional and preventative aspects of health and wellbeing.

~

**SPH**: *What are some of the things we can do to support or optimise the 'brain health' of a person with Alzheimer's?*

**RS**: We look at the health of the whole person – liver function, heart function, circulation, metabolic and hormonal functions. All of these support good health generally, and have an influence on the brain.

For a whole variety of physical reasons there may be a deterioration in the level and variety of nutrients in the body generally, and in the efficiency with which they are reaching and being metabolised by the brain cells in particular. Many of us don't have sufficient levels of important nutrients anyhow, but where there is any evidence of reduced cognitive or brain function it is particularly important to do what we can.

So we pay attention to the nutritional use of antioxidants, and to minerals shown to be important in brain function and repair. Some of the things that can be helpful here are vitamin C, vitamin E, zinc, selenium, chromium, free fatty acids found in fish and some other oils, and B vitamins, especially vitamin B12.

Often therapeutic doses of herbs can be useful. There are several that have been shown to support micro-circulation and cognitive function, including Gingko biloba, rosemary and bacopa [also known as brahmi].

We also look to correct any other imbalances that may be affecting the person's health and brain function. In Hazel's case, for example, she had a mild hypothyroidism that was reducing her overall function and contributing to some of her symptoms. When we stabilised that, her wellbeing improved and stabilised for a while.

If there comes a point where there is clearly a progressive cognitive decline I discuss it with my patients, and maybe their family, and recommend that we have it investigated further by whatever specialist means seem appropriate in their case. If the diagnosis is Alzheimer's, then there are some drugs that can be useful for some people, and are definitely worth trying, although they're not a 'magic bullet' for the condition. And we continue, of course, with all the supports for general health and 'brain health' that are appropriate for the individual patient.

**SPH**: *What about other less directly 'medical' factors?*

**RS**: It is important to support an active and healthy life generally and, particularly, continued cognitive stimulation by participating in activities which engage the brain – chess, crosswords, playing or listening to music, social interaction – anything which the person with dementia can do and enjoy. Just because cognitive function may be gradually degenerating does not mean they should go into a 'premature shutdown'. It is important for family and carers to do what they can to support active participation and interaction. I will talk with the patient and the family to help support good diet, good exercise, social interaction and a positive attitude.

It is also important to help the person be comfortable, to do your best to remove unnecessary stresses. Love and care make a big difference to this. Hopefully we can care for the person with Alzheimer's in the way that they once cared for us – although sometimes you need to draw a line and say 'Well, we can't do any more.' And if there comes a stage when they need to be in a nursing home, then a good range of activities and interests should be available there for them, and a caring approach to their needs, whatever they are at that stage.

# Where to Turn for Help

ALZHEIMER'S AUSTRALIA IS THE national peak body for people living with dementia, their families and carers. It provides information, support, education services and advocacy and has branches in each state and territory. Membership is open to anybody concerned about dementia.

It aims to give people living with Alzheimer's disease and other forms of dementia the respect they deserve and the support they need. It works hard to raise community awareness and understanding of Alzheimer's disease and other dementia conditions. Community support in the form of donations and sponsorship, as well as bequests, is vital to the continuation and growth of the work of Alzheimer's Australia. Donations are tax deductible.

The organisation provides a range of flexible and sensitive services including a Dementia Helpline; a network of support groups for people with dementia and their carers; carer education programs; and private, confidential counselling services. It also provides training, information and resources to service providers, including healthcare workers and care organisations, to enable them to appropriately support people living with dementia, and their carers and families. (Services offered differ slightly from state to state.)

Alzheimer's Australia has a range of resources that cover all aspects of dementia care, from first symptoms and diagnosis to the latest information on medical treatment and research, and practical management strategies.

**The Dementia Helpline number is 1800 639 331.**

You can call this number from anywhere in Australia 24 hours a day. The helpline is staffed by trained and experienced advisers, many with personal experience in dementia care. An interpreter service is available on 131 450.

The Alzheimer's Australia website offers detailed information, fact sheets, event calendars and more. It is at: www.alzheimers.org.au.

You can call the national helpline or access the website to find out about information and services in your area, or contact your local Alzheimer's Australia branch:

**ACT**
Phone: (02) 6254 5544
Email: admin@alzheimers act.asn.au
Fax: (02) 6254 2522
Frewin Place
Scullin ACT 2614

**NORTHERN TERRITORY**
Phone: (08) 8948 5228
Email: admin.alz@octa4.net.au
Fax: (08) 8948 5229
Nightcliff Community Centre
Suite 3/18 Bauhinia Street
Nightcliff NT 0810

**NSW**
Phone: (02) 9805 0100
Email: admin@alznsw.asn.au
Fax: (02) 9805 1665
Macquarie Hospital Campus
Cox's Road Entrance
North Ryde NSW 2113

**QUEENSLAND**
Phone: (07) 5574 6224
Email: info@alzqld.asn.au
Fax: (07) 5571 5987
90 Allied Drive
Arundel QLD 4214

**SOUTH AUSTRALIA**
Phone: (08) 8372 2100
Email: alzsa@alzheimerssa.asn.au
Fax: (08) 8338 3390
27 Conyngham Street
Glenside SA 5065

**TASMANIA**
Phone: (03) 6278 9897
Email: debbie.slater@alztas.asn.au
Fax: (03) 6278 9878
The Old Vicarage
St John's Avenue
New Town TAS 7008

**VICTORIA**
Phone: (03) 9815 7800
Email: alz@alzvic.asn.au
Fax: (03) 9815 7801
98–104 Riversdale Road
Hawthorn VIC 3122

**WESTERN AUSTRALIA**
Phone: (08) 9388 2800
Email: alzwa@alzheimers.asn.au
Fax: (08) 9388 2739
Mary Chester Centre
9 Bedbrook Place
Shenton Park WA 6008

# How Do I Know If I'm Getting Alzheimer's Disease?

IF YOU ARE WORRIED about your memory, or feeling forgetful or confused, Alzheimer's Australia suggests investigating the problem further. Finding out what is wrong is the first step to getting help. Changes in memory and thinking have a number of possible causes that may include stress, depression, pain, chronic illness, medication or alcohol and sometimes early dementia. Major changes in memory, however, are not normal at any age and should be taken seriously. If you are experiencing these kinds of difficulties it is better to see your doctor sooner rather than later.

Following is a list of common concerns about changes in memory and thinking. Tick those that apply to you. If you have identified any areas of concern by marking them as 'sometimes' or 'often' on the list, follow it up with your doctor.

Do note, however, that this list of concerns is provided as a guide only for discussion with your doctor. The presence of these changes does not necessarily mean you have, or will develop, Alzheimer's disease or any other type of dementia.

I have trouble remembering events that have happened recently.

❒ Rarely ❒ Sometimes ❒ Often

I have trouble finding the right word.

❒ Rarely ❒ Sometimes ❒ Often

I have trouble remembering the day or date.

❒ Rarely ❒ Sometimes ❒ Often

I forget where things are usually kept.

❒ Rarely ❒ Sometimes ❒ Often

I have difficulty adjusting to any changes in my day-to-day routine.

❒ Rarely ❒ Sometimes ❒ Often

I have problems understanding magazine or newspaper articles or following a story in a book or on TV.

❒ Rarely ❒ Sometimes ❒ Often

I find it hard to follow and join in conversations, particularly in groups.

❐ Rarely ❐ Sometimes ❐ Often

I have problems handling financial matters, such as banking or calculating change.

❐ Rarely ❐ Sometimes ❐ Often

I have difficulty with other everyday activities such as remembering how long it is between visits from family or friends or cooking a meal I have always cooked.

❐ Rarely ❐ Sometimes ❐ Often

I am losing interest in activities I'd normally enjoy.

❐ Rarely ❐ Sometimes ❐ Often

I have difficulty thinking through problems.

❐ Rarely ❐ Sometimes ❐ Often

Family and/or friends have commented about my poor memory.

❐ Rarely ❐ Sometimes ❐ Often

# Useful Books and Videos

SUE RECOMMENDS:

*The Tibetan Book of Living and Dying* by Sogyal Rinpoche.

ALZHEIMER'S AUSTRALIA RECOMMENDS:

**General books about dementia**

*The problem of dementia in Australia*, Australian Government Publishing Service, ACT. A useful overview of dementia and dementia care in Australia.

*Alzheimer's disease: The answers you need* by Helen Davies and Michael Jensen. A guidebook written for people in the early stages of Alzheimer's disease and their caregivers.

*Keys to understanding Alzheimer's disease* by Gisele P Wolf Klein and Arnold P Levy. In non-technical language, the authors explain symptoms, advise on care strategies, offer moral support, suggest sources of outside help and generally treat this difficult subject with both intelligence and sensitivity.

*Alzheimer's: A caregiver's guide and sourcebook* by Howard Greutzner. This is a useful and practical look at changed behaviours, underlying causes and self-help.

*The carer experience: Information and ideas for carers of people with dementia* by the Commonwealth Department of Health and Family Services. This Australian book is available free of charge from the Commonwealth Government or Alzheimer's Association.

*When I grow too old to dream* by Gerry Naughtin and Terry Laidler. This Australian book gives details regarding dementia and stories from carers on their experiences of caring.

*Dementia with dignity: A handbook for carers* by Barbara Sherman. A well-organised, positive book, with a systematic approach to analysing and understanding changed behaviours.

*The 36-hour day: A family guide to caring for persons with Alzheimer's disease, related dementing illnesses, and memory loss in later life* by Nancy Mace and Peter Rabins. An in-depth guide to home care of people with dementia. Practical advice is supported by specific examples covering relevant medical, financial and emotional issues.

*Alzheimer's: Caring for your loved one, caring for yourself* by Sharon Fish with Susan Cuthbert. Sharon Fish has brought both personal and professional experience in caring for people with dementia to this useful and compassionate book.

*Taking care of the caregivers: For families and others who care for people with Alzheimer's disease and other forms of dementia* by D Jeanne Roberts. This workbook attempts to assist carers to recognise their own needs, to deal with feelings and stress created by caring and to improve communication skills.

*Understanding difficult behaviours: Some practical suggestions for coping with Alzheimer's disease and related illnesses* by Anne Robinson, Beth Spencer and Laurie White. A very systematic and well explained look at changed behaviours in dementia.

*Finger Food for Independence* by Lois Newton and Alan Stewart. A useful and clear guide to food that is easy to prepare, serve and eat for people with dementia.

## Books written by people with dementia

*Who will I be when I die?* by Christine Boden. Christine Boden was first diagnosed with Alzheimer's disease at age 46 and then rediagnosed with frontotemporal dementia at age 49. This is the first book written by an Australian with dementia and offers a unique insight into her battle with the disease.

*Living in the labyrinth: A personal journey through the maze of Alzheimer's* by Diana Friel McGowan. An autobiographical book which tells of the author's struggle with the effects of Alzheimer's disease and offers the reader an insight into the world of dementia.

(Also useful is the cover story of *The Bulletin* magazine, 22 June 2004, 'Thanks for the Memories' by Diana Bagnall, which includes interviews with several people with dementia.)

## Carers telling their own stories

*A Funny Thing Happened on the Way to the Nursing Home* by Jim Connor. A true and touching account of a man caring for his wife who has dementia. The story contains pathos, humour and hope.

*My Mother is My Daughter* by Claire N Laishley. A moving story about the changes in the relationship between a daughter-carer and her mother.

*Forget-me-not: Caring for an Alzheimer's patient* by Jan Charker. Jan Charker tells the story, with much love and compassion, of caring for her husband, Dave, who had early onset Alzheimer's disease.

*Caring for Maria: An experience of successfully coping with Alzheimer's disease* by Bernard Heywood. Based on diaries written to reduce the stress of caring, this account is honest and down-to-earth in its approach. It tells of Maria's reversion to her native language (German), her early paranoia and her great inner strength.

*Catch a falling star: Living with Alzheimer's* by Betty Spohr with Jean Valens Bullard. This book is in the form of short diary entries and sketches describing the course of Alzheimer's disease in Betty's husband. At the end of each section there is a list of suggestions for coping.

*Where did Mary go? A loving husband's struggle with Alzheimer's* by Frank A Wall. This book describes the author's emotions, stress and practical approach in caring for his wife.

## Books aimed at young people

*Fading memories: An adolescent's guide to Alzheimer's disease* by The American Health Assistance Foundation. This book gives basic information on Alzheimer's disease, care of people with the disease and unusual behaviours. Included are essays written by adolescents who have experienced living with someone with Alzheimer's disease.

*The long and winding road – a young person's guide to dementia* by Jane Gilliard. This short book gives a brief overview of dementia and its effect on the person with dementia, and young people who have an affected family.

*Understanding dementia: A guide for young carers* by Kate Fearnley. This book sets out the information simply and clearly, but goes into more detail than most books written for young people. It includes some information on types of dementia, including some rarer dementias as well as practical suggestions for coping, looking after yourself and dealing with feelings.

*The Smell of Chocolate* by Barbara McGuire. Produced by Alzheimer's Australia WA, this illustrated book is designed to help children better understand what is happening to elderly relatives who develop dementia, using the relationship of Ben and his grandfather, Pog.

## Videos

*You must remember this.* Information on Alzheimer's disease is interspersed with carer stories in this well-made Australian video.

*Understanding Alzheimer's.* This video provides an introduction to Alzheimer's disease, risk factors, behaviours and issues of concern for carers.

*Brain and behaviour.* In this video Dr Helen Creasey explains brain function and dysfunction, and changes in behaviour.

*Dementia with dignity.* This video examines ways to manage dementia, including a section on responding to difficult situations and disruptive behaviour.

*A time to care: helping people with dementia and their families.* This video explains the symptoms and effects of dementia and provides information on caring at home for a relative or friend.

*No easy answers.* This video looks at changed behaviours such as wandering, aggression, sexual behaviours and catastrophic reactions.

*Alzheimer's 101: The basics for caregiving.* This video looks at topics such as stress, communication, problem behaviours and personal care. It provides useful, practical strategies for carers.

*Men caring: A common bond.* This Australian video highlights the challenges facing a group of men caring for their partners with dementia.

*Poppy's head.* A well-made and appealing Australian video which looks at dementia through the relationship of 15-year-old Zeb and his grandfather.

*Someone I love has Alzheimer's disease.* In this video children aged 7 to 15 who are involved in caring for a family member discuss their feelings and opinions in an open manner.

# Acknowledgements

**SPH and HF:**

Thanks to all who have contributed directly to this book:

Professor Henry Brodaty, Lewis Kaplan, Wendy McCarthy, Sue Spence, Ros Strong, Dr Richard Schloeffel, Jean-Paul Bell, Faye Crampton, Mary Roddy, Marilyn MacArthur, Nicky Heyward-Wright and all the helpful staff at Alzheimer's Australia;

Everyone who so generously wrote and emailed Hazel after *Australian Story*, including those who have allowed us to share their stories here;

The volunteers at Alzheimer's Australia; all the medicos and researchers now, and in the future, who care for patients and their families, and seek to solve the mysteries of Alzheimer's; and

Sue Jamieson, Electronics Today at Lane Cove, and Dictation World at Parramatta.

**SPH:**

To all the people in Mum's life, and in mine, who somehow share the journey – too many, as they say, to mention. But . . .

Thanks, firstly, to those closest – Sophie, Ben and Jan. My global family.

I wish also to personally thank the many friends, the kind and wise souls, who have sustained us – Wendy McCarthy, Prue Watson, Bob and Blanche, Linda Graham McCann, Jane and Paul Munro, Helen Grasswill, Gail, Annie Farley, Deb Homburg, Nicole Murray, Philip Heath and the wonderful staff at St Andrew's, Jeff Morrison and the Body of Work crew, Roie Paul, Sue Burton, Ian Wallace, the Concert Consorts, and Jarek Alexander (for the house!).

My beloved Rigpa Sangha friends – Ross Mackay, Wendy Wright, Chris McCarthy, Meg Hart, Kerry Carmody, and so many others.

The friends who rallied during that year from hell – Eve and Daniel, Robert Browne, David and Donna, Rachel and Glen, Judy and Michael, the Men's Group.

The members of the advisory board of the Hazel Hawke Alzheimer's Research and Care Fund, and all those who have kindly donated to its work.

Thanks also to the lovely Hazel Flynn – a more patient yet persistent co-writer I cannot imagine. And to the crew at Pan Macmillan – Tom, Karen, Jeannine, et al – who were confident that there was a story worth telling, and that we could tell it.

Lastly, a special word of thanks to Sogyal Rinpoche, and to all he represents and conveys. I couldn't have done this without his wisdom and warmth.